PENGUIN BOOKS

THE SCIENTIFIC INDIAN

A.P.J. Abdul Kalam was one of India's most distinguished scientists, responsible for the development of the country's first satellite launch vehicle and the operationalization of strategic missiles. He also pioneered India Vision 2020, a road map for transforming India. The President of India between 2002 and 2007, Dr Kalam was awarded honorary doctorates from thirty-eight universities and the country's three highest civilian honours—the Padma Bhushan (1981), Padma Vibhushan (1990) and Bharat Ratna (1997). A prolific and bestselling author, he conducted lectures on societal development in many international institutes and was involved in research on different societal missions. Dr Kalam passed away in July 2015.

Yagnaswami Sundara Rajan is a well-recognized authority on technology development, business management and society linkages. He has held various positions of responsibility related to science and technology between 1988 and 2002, and has shaped key policies and implemented several R&D projects with industry participation. He is currently principal adviser, CII.

BY THE SAME AUTHORS

India 2020: A Vision for the New Millennium

Kolkata, Park Street
December 2017
Oxford Bookstore

THE SCIENTIFIC INDIAN

A Twenty-first Century Guide to the
World Around Us

A.P.J. ABDUL KALAM

and

Y.S. RAJAN

PENGUIN BOOKS

PENGUIN BOOKS

Published by the Penguin Group

Penguin Books India Pvt. Ltd, 7th Floor, Infinity Tower C, DLF Cyber City, Gurgaon 122 002, Haryana, India

Penguin Group (USA) Inc., 375 Hudson Street, New York, New York 10014, USA

Penguin Group (Canada), 90 Eglinton Avenue East, Suite 700, Toronto, Ontario, M4P 2Y3, Canada

Penguin Books Ltd, 80 Strand, London WC2R 0RL, England

Penguin Ireland, 25 St Stephen's Green, Dublin 2, Ireland (a division of Penguin Books Ltd)

Penguin Group (Australia), 707 Collins Street, Melbourne, Victoria 3008, Australia

Penguin Group (NZ), 67 Apollo Drive, Rosedale, Auckland 0632, New Zealand

Penguin Books (South Africa) (Pty) Ltd, Block D, Rosebank Office Park, 181 Jan Smuts Avenue, Parktown North, Johannesburg 2193, South Africa

Penguin Books Ltd, Registered Offices: 80 Strand, London WC2R 0RL, England

First published in Viking by Penguin Books India 2010
Published in Penguin Books 2011

Copyright © A.P.J. Abdul Kalam and Y.S. Rajan 2010

12 11

ISBN 9780143416876

The views and opinions expressed in this book are the authors' own and the facts are as reported by them, and the publishers are not in any way liable for the same.

Typeset in Californian FB by SÜRYA, New Delhi
Printed at Thomson Press India Ltd, New Delhi

A PENGUIN RANDOM HOUSE COMPANY

This book is dedicated to all those who are curious about nature and life and bold enough to seek new knowledge and endure the rigorous methods of science

CONTENTS

ACKNOWLEDGEMENTS

This book is the product of a lifelong process of learning, which still continues. The authors would like to thank the various sources—books, journals, other media and individuals, too numerous to list—that they have drawn on and been inspired by.

Y.S. Rajan in particular would like to thank the authors, publishers and institutes whose books, publications and websites have been mentioned in various chapters.

In addition, Y.S. Rajan would like to express his loving gratitude to his wife Gomati, who has given him support in his intellectual meanderings for over four decades, and to his second son Dr Vikram Rajan for critically evaluating many of his approaches and insights. He would also like to thank the Confederation of Indian Industries (CII) for providing him the necessary environment for his creative pursuits over the past five years, and Suraj Anandan who typed up the handwritten manuscript patiently but quickly, and made some interesting observations as well.

Finally, the authors would like to thank Udayan Mitra, Publishing Director at Penguin Books India, for his steadfast belief in this book and for his unstinted editorial and moral support.

SPACE

Chapter 1

SPACE: THE FINAL FRONTIER

If you ask where space begins, it is difficult to give a precise answer. Just above the surface of the Earth is the atmosphere, without which life would not exist on Earth. The thick blanket called the troposphere, which extends to about 15 km above the Earth's surface, protects life on Earth from the harmful ultraviolet rays of the Sun and also gives us the beautiful optical spectrum of the rainbow.

What are ultraviolet rays? You are aware of VIBGYOR (Violet, Indigo, Blue, Green, Yellow, Orange, Red), the seven colours that form the Sun's optical band of emission. You see these colours in a rainbow—a rare sight these days in most urban areas due to dust and excessive pollution—but you can see a similar colour ray-spilling if you keep a bucket filled with water out in the sun and put a thin layer of kerosene or oil on the water. Or you can split the Sun's rays with a prism and see the seven colours. Of the colours in VIBGYOR visible to us, red has the lowest energy in the optical region; the colours increase in energy from red to violet.

Below red in energy are the infra-red rays. Infra-red is equivalent to the heat rays that we cannot see but can sense through our skin. Below infra-red in energy are microwave rays (which are used to cook or warm food in a microwave oven), and further down are radio waves (which form the basis of TV and radio reception).

Higher in energy than violet, and invisible to us, are ultraviolet (UV) rays. In the upper region of high-energy rays—generally called electromagnetic rays (EMRs)—above ultraviolet rays are X-rays, then gamma rays. In a nuclear reaction in a nuclear power station or during the explosion of a nuclear bomb, you will have lots of gamma rays. The Sun emits them too, as do other stars in the cosmos.

There are whole sets of scientific researches studying the Sun's emissions and relating these to diverse phenomena on Earth. This is still an active research area.

Above the troposphere there are several layers of atmosphere discovered through researches, mostly over the twentieth century. Some of the early rocket experiments from Thumba during the 1960s, for which Dr Kalam provided the rocket services as an ISRO engineer, were aimed at studying these layers. Y.S. Rajan used to work as a research scholar then at the Physical Research Laboratory, Ahmedabad, and would discuss these experiments with Dr Kalam.

As we go upwards from the surface of the Earth, the atmosphere becomes less dense, that is, the number of molecules of various constituents of the air (nitrogen, oxygen, carbon dioxide, water vapour etc.) decreases. Even 2 km above the surface, the atmosphere is noticeably thinner. If you go to Ladakh or to the upper regions of the Himalayas the air is less dense than in the plains. The air there has less oxygen, and we need to adjust to it. When you go to Leh, which is at a height of 3,300 metres, you will be asked to take a day's rest before you move about, to allow your body to acclimatize itself to the thinner air. If you go much higher, you may need external oxygen support.

When you travel by air you will hear the captain announce that the plane will fly at an altitude of around 30,000 ft (about 9 km). This is the normal height at which commercial aircraft fly. Military surveillance and air force planes go much higher, to a height of 15 km or more. Over 15 km from the surface of the Earth, the atmosphere is much thinner; this layer of the atmosphere is called the stratosphere. Very small numbers of air molecules are to be found there, but it is still not a complete vacuum. There are still enough air molecules to balance the aircraft. Such heights are still part of airspace. For the airspace above a country, the government of that country has sovereignty, just as it has over the land, the soil below the ground, and the waters extending to a certain distance from the shore. This is why it is necessary to get approval from the countries concerned before flying over them. There are international agreements for civilian aircraft to fly through the airspace of various countries. For military aircraft one has to take permission to fly over another country's territory. If a plane enters a country's airspace without permission, it can be shot down. That is why military units use unmanned automated vehicles (UAVs) on stealth missions, when they are flying through an airspace without permission.

As we go upwards from the surface of the Earth, the atmospheric density keeps decreasing gradually. Do you know why? The further the air molecules are from the Earth's surface, the less the Earth's gravity is able to pull them down. They also absorb the Sun's energy and become more dynamic. They move faster, and many of them start losing their molecular status. Due to the effect of UV rays, X-rays and gamma rays, the air molecules are broken down into nuclei, electrons and ions.

Beyond 30 km from the surface of the Earth it is difficult to operate conventional aircraft or balloons as the air is very rare. These upper layers of the atmosphere, starting around 50 km and going up to 300 km, form the ionosphere. Certain frequencies of radio transmission depend on the ionosphere; till the last quarter of the twentieth century, these bands of radio frequency waves were crucial for civilian and military use. The global coverage of radio was brought about by AM (amplitude modulation) radio stations like the BBC, Voice of America, Radio Moscow, Radio

Ceylon and others that used High Frequency (HF) and Very High Frequency (VHF) waves. Today's children won't know much about AM radio, since space communication (which is satellite-based) has taken over global coverage and for urban areas much higher radio frequencies that work over short distances—direct straight lines like the optical part of EMRs, FM radio, cell phone networks etc.—are used. These work only up to the horizon, as seen from the height of the transmission tower. Space communication satellites are like huge invisible towers 36,000 km tall. More about these later.

The ionosphere (even at a height of 300 km from the surface of the Earth) still has a number of molecules, ions and electrons. These have high speeds because of their high energies derived from the Sun. Also, the ions and electrons interact with the Earth's magnetic field and acquire considerable speed in certain directions. Therefore if satellites were placed in orbit at a height of 300 km, they would be hit by many of these molecules, ions and electrons, which would lead to considerable friction. The satellites would slow down and also get heated. They would gradually descend in orbit and eventually enter the lower levels of the atmosphere and get burnt up like meteorites. To work efficiently, satellites have to be placed in orbit at a greater height of 400 or 500 km. The higher they are placed, the lesser the molecules and friction, and the longer the life of the satellites in orbit.

The space beyond the atmosphere—which consists of the layers of space called the troposphere, stratosphere and ionosphere—is called outer space. Those concerned with space technology and applications mostly deal with outer space—though they need to be aware of the lower segments of space, as well as the Earth and its rotation, to be able to launch and plan satellite missions.

India started its tryst with outer space in 1980, with the launch of the satellite named Rohini with the indigenously made satellite launch vehicle SLV-3. It was a proud day for India when it became the seventh spacefaring nation—that is, a nation that is successfully able to place a satellite in orbit in outer space—after the Soviet

Union, USA, UK, France, China and Japan. There are more countries that have joined this exclusive group since, the most recent being Iran and North Korea.

Most of Dr Kalam's life has been spent in activities connected to launching into space: he always thinks in terms of space. He describes even his age as the number of orbits taken round the Sun, rather than in years. His dream of making India a spacefaring nation did not come true easily. He was close to completing forty-nine orbits around the Sun when the first successful launch of SLV-3 took place. Here is what he said in his address to the members of the ISRO community at the Satish Dhawan Space Centre, Sriharikota on 10 October 2003, when he was close to completing seventy-two orbits.

———————

This is my first visit to the SHAR centre after it has been named after Prof. Satish Dhawan, one of the greatest sons of our country. I cherish every moment of my privileged association with this great technologist, teacher, visionary, administrator and above all a wonderful and noble human being. SHAR symbolizes many things to me. It represents the consummation of visions, concepts and high technology; the confluence of disciplines and more so the meeting of human minds. You have launched seventeen launch vehicles from here and will be attempting the eighteenth one a week from now.

As I stand here today, many events come back to me. It was on 9 October 1971 that the country witnessed the first-ever launch of a sounding rocket—125 mm in diameter—from SHAR, less than three years after the decision was made to set up the launching station at SHAR. I recollect the pioneering efforts by many stalwarts in building the launch pad and associated facilities. Very soon SPROB was taking shape and other facilities like STEX came up. I recall the long nights when I and my team used to discuss the processing and static testing of motors for SLV-3. The untiring efforts by the VSSC and SHAR teams ensured that the four types of motors went through their qualification satisfactorily. Parallely, the launch complex facilities were being set up. Along with that, several mechanisms of dealing with a mission, the mission readiness reviews, and the launch authorization board were getting evolved and implemented. The excitement of launch campaigns, the tension of the countdown, the emotions of a launch have all become history and have been deeply etched in my memory. The magnanimity of Prof. Dhawan in dealing with the failure of the first launch and his motivating and leading us towards success in the very next flight is one of the basic foundations of a great ISRO culture.

At every stage, the SLV-3 team was blessed with some extraordinarily courageous people. Shri Sivakaminathan was bringing the C-band transponder from Trivandrum to SHAR for integration with SLV-3. The SLV-3 launch schedule was dependant on the arrival and integration of this equipment. On landing at the Madras airport, the aircraft in which Sivakami was travelling skidded and overshot the runway. Dense smoke engulfed the aircraft. Everyone jumped out of the aircraft through the emergency exit and desperately fought to save themselves—all except Sivakami who stayed in the aircraft till he removed the transponder from his baggage. He was among the last few persons to emerge from the smoke and he was holding the transponder close to his chest. This was the level of dedication and attachment to the project, because people owned this project.

I have witnessed several successful flights and a few failures on this range. The first mission was a failure but we recovered fast, and we were ready for the second mission. 18 July 1980 is a memorable day for the entire space community of India. This was the day the space scientists put a 40 kg satellite (Rohini) in a low-Earth orbit through SLV-3 which took off at 0805 hrs; within minutes the satellite was in orbit. This was a great accomplishment for our scientists, especially after an unsuccessful earlier mission on 10 August 1979.

There was jubilation all around. People were thrilled. They were shouting, hugging and lifting each other up and were emotionally charged. This was the time Prof. Dhawan took me aside and said that we should go to a quiet place. The two of us went to the launch pad and sat on the launcher. We watched the waves of the Bay of Bengal in silence. After a few minutes Prof. Dhawan said to me: 'Kalam, you know you have been working hard for the last eight years. You encountered a number of problems and failures. You faced them all with utmost courage, patience and perseverance. For all the efforts that you put in, today we have got the results. I want to thank you for your excellent work. I will remember it and cherish it.' I had never come across such a beautiful day. In the middle of the din of the loud jubilation of the entire space community, Prof. Dhawan and I were enjoying the intrinsic beauty of the mega-event.

Why is it so difficult to place a satellite in orbit?

If you throw a stone upwards, it falls back to the ground. This is due to the Earth's gravitational pull. An airplane, with lots of energy in store to defy the Earth's gravity, has to come down too before the fuel is finished. Even an air balloon sent upwards will eventually come down.

Powerful rockets fired upwards into space are no different— they too are subject to gravity. So shooting a rocket upwards is not enough. One has to find a way to ensure that the satellite obtains adequate velocity (speed with direction) in order to be injected into an orbit 400 km or more above the Earth's surface.

That was the mission of SLV-3, the first successful satellite launch vehicle project undertaken by the Indian Space Research Organization (ISRO).

Let us now look at the tasks of a launch vehicle.

First it has to get out of the thick blanket of the troposphere. Though its final position when placing the satellite in orbit has to be almost parallel to the Earth's surface, if the trajectory of the launch vehicle is slanted from the beginning, it will have a longer distance to travel through the troposphere, and will have to face too much friction and endure too much heat. The shortest way through the troposphere is straight up. So the launch vehicle goes vertically up till it clears the troposphere.

Once it has cleared the troposphere, the launch vehicle begins to slant slowly. This is called 'pitching'. It is done slowly as the vehicle is at high speed. When the launch vehicle reaches the right height of the intended satellite orbit, the control system provides the satellite the right direction and speed, and it is dispatched from the launch vehicle into space.

The satellite is free. Its own centrifugal force and the Earth's gravitational pull balance each other. The satellite falls into orbit around the Earth, just like the Moon which is around 380,000 km away from the Earth, and takes twenty-seven days to complete its orbit. A satellite around 500 km from the Earth's surface takes one and a half hours to go around the Earth.

What is centrifugal force? Newton's first law tells us: Every body persists in its state of being at rest or of continuous motion, unless it is compelled to change its state by an external force.

If you are travelling in a car or a bus that is going at high speed and takes a sharp turn, you will feel a push away from the centre of the circle that the arc of the turning vehicle is drawing. This is due to centrifugal force.

Here is an interesting experiment. Take a small bucket half-filled with water. Lift it up by the handle and start whirling it in a circle, making sure that the motion is uninterrupted. You will find that the water does not fall even when the bucket is almost upside down, with the water facing the ground. The centrifugal force matches the Earth's gravity, so the water does not fall!

A similar thing happens when a satellite is placed with the right velocity and direction in the right orbit. The Earth pulls the satellite down towards it, while the centrifugal force pulls it away, just as you are simultaneously pulled in and pushed away in the sharp turning vehicle. The two forces cancel each other out; the satellite continues in orbit—as per Newton's law.

The SLV-3, launched by Dr Kalam and his team, including Y.S. Rajan, had the task of placing Rohini in an orbit higher than 400 km from the Earth. There is something called a 'rocket equation' which describes how the rocket would be propelled upward to achieve the desired orbit.

The SLV-3 had four stages of rockets. Why?

It is very difficult to achieve the orbit and direction required with a single-stage rocket. A multistage rocket has several advantages. When the bottom stage of the rocket is ignited, the thrust of the burning gases from the slowly burning fuel of the rocket goes downwards and creates an opposite force that is directed straight upwards, working against the force of gravity. The initial force is just above that of the force of gravity so that the rocket has a gentle lift-off; then it speeds up.

As the rocket rises upwards, more gases burn, which leads to its acceleration. In addition, since some propellant has already been burnt, some mass of the rocket has already reduced. So the rocket is lighter now than it was at lift-off. The force of burning gases remains the same, so the rocket gathers speed and keeps accelerating. The more numbered stages a rocket has, the more empty shells can be dropped off after the use of each stage of fuel, thus further lightening the weight (mass) to be carried by the rocket.

You may have noticed at a traffic light that for two vehicles with the same power, it is easier for the lighter vehicle to gather speed. When climbing a steep slope, a cycle-rickshaw driver will sometimes ask the passenger to get down or get down himself and push the rickshaw. This is to reduce the 'payload' to be pushed. A rocket operates on the same principle.

It was the fourth stage of SLV-3 that provided the final boost which rocket engineers call Delta V, the additional velocity needed to reach the right orbit height which is determined by the 'rocket equation'. With the rocket at the right velocity and the right height, the satellite is separated from the launch vehicle. At this point the centrifugal force which pushes the satellite out of the orbit and the Earth's gravitational pull on it are exactly balanced, and the satellite falls into orbit. The Moon orbits the Earth following the same principle, and all the planets follow their orbits around the Sun as per the same law of physics. For geosynchronous satellites like INSAT, the orbit height from the Earth's surface is adjusted in such a way that it takes twenty-four hours to go around the Earth. It is exactly like two trains travelling on parallel tracks at the same speed: with respect to each they look stationary.

Every rocket is designed to lift a satellite with a specified mass (weight) to a particular height and direction. This sizing of the launch vehicle is known as Mission Planning.

SLV-3, which placed the satellite Rohini in orbit, was a pioneer. ISRO's current satellite launch vehicles—PSLV, GSLV etc.—are much heavier and far more complex and sophisticated, not merely in terms of propellants but also in terms of guidance systems, controls, telemetry, materials etc. They are far more automated than SLV-3 was. Even an hour ahead of the launch, computers take over. It is somewhat like operating modern aircraft; after the flight reaches a certain height, automatic controls take over from manual control. It is because of these automated capabilities that India is now able to undertake a complex mission like the Chandrayaan-1 launch.

What are polar and geosynchronous satellites?

The Earth is like a globe that is a little flat at the two tops, like an orange. The two 'tops' are the polar regions, the North Pole and the South Pole. The Earth rotates on its North–South axis at a great speed (about 1570 km/hour). Without this rotation we would not have the day–night effect. Our twenty-four-hour day is the result of the Earth's rotation on its own axis; this is why at a given spot on

Earth we see the Sun entering into our sight at sunrise and disappearing from sight at sunset.

While the Earth's diameter (about 12,750 km) is small compared to the distance between the Earth and the Sun (approx 149,476,000 km), it is not insignificant. The amount of the Sun's energy received on the equator is more than that received at the poles. This is because the Sun's rays fall differently at different latitudes—most strongly at the equator but decreasing steadily in higher latitudes. As we move away from the equator towards the north or the south the weather becomes milder; thus Kanyakumari is hotter than Kashmir. This is called latitudinal difference.

There is a unique thing about a longitude, however: the Sun shines all along a longitude at the same time, and this is repeated every twenty-four hours. So if the orbit of a satellite runs parallel to a longitude, from the South Pole to the North Pole and then back again to the South Pole along the other side of the Earth, that orbit is in synchronization with the Sun. A satellite in synchronous orbit with the Sun has to go through the poles just as a longitude does, and so such a satellite is called a polar satellite.

Why do we need polar satellites? All Earth observation systems—assessing soils, forests, water, clouds etc.—depend on comparison of scattered or reflected sunlight; so it is essential to take pictures under the same light conditions. If a picture of your garden is taken in the evening light and another at noon, you cannot really make much of a visual comparison between the two—one will be too bright, the other too dark. This is where a sun synchronous satellite becomes important.*

The Indian Remote Sensing satellite (IRS) is a sun synchronous satellite. The Polar Satellite Launch Vehicle (PSLV) was specially

---

*What we have given here is very simple conceptual description. In actuality there are a number of complex calculations involved; while a polar path is important for Earth observation satellites, not all polar orbits are fully sun synchronous.

developed by ISRO to launch the IRS satellites. PSLVs are much larger and heavier rockets than SLV-3. The overall weight of a PSLV at lift-off is about 295 tonnes (295,000 kg) while the overall weight of SLV-3 at lift-off was about 17 tonnes (17,000 kg). The rocket that launched Chandrayaan-1 was an augmented version of the PSLV.

The INSAT (Indian National Satellite) system also has a series of satellites which provide for various communication needs like telephones, television transmission, massive data transfers etc. These are geosynchronous or geostationary satellites.

In 1983, when the first INSAT satellite was made operational (INSAT-1A failed and it was the second in the series, INSAT-1B, which was the first operational geostationary satellite providing services to India), it helped to double our telecommunication capability within one and a half years. Such is the speed of satellite communication. This is because one satellite can link up to several receiving ground stations simultaneously; there is no need for any intermediate cable connections. One can reach even the remotest area with ease.

You would already have guessed that a geostationary satellite cannot be a polar satellite. The Earth rotates from west to east (that is why the Sun 'rises' in the east and 'sets' in the west). Therefore something moving on a north–south route cannot be stationary with respect to Earth. It will be stationary with respect to Earth only if it moves parallel to the equatorial line at the same speed as Earth, that is taking twenty-four hours to complete an orbit. You will remember that the centrifugal force active on the satellite when it is placed in orbit has to balance the gravitational pull on it. For a twenty-four-hour orbit the required orbital height is about 36,000 km above the surface of the Earth. If you could sit inside a geosynchronous satellite you would see the Earth as stationary.

What is the advantage of having a satellite at such a height? If you have placed a satellite in a geostationary orbit, it is equivalent to erecting an invisible tower 36,000 km high. We know that the higher the telecom tower, the better the coverage. A geostationary satellite gives us that capability. If we put a meteorological camera on the satellite, it can also perform weather monitoring functions from its great height, giving us twenty-four-hour coverage. In times of emergence of cyclones, you would have seen INSAT pictures a few days before the cyclone hits, showing the pressure depression over the sea, its progress path etc. This can often turn out to be life-saving information.

The launch of geostationary satellites requires much higher energy than that of a near-Earth satellite because the satellite has to be taken to a 36,000 km high orbit. That is why GSLVs (Geosynchronous Satellite Launch Vehicles) have to be much heavier than the near-Earth launching PSLVs (Polar Satellite Launch Vehicles). ISRO's GSLV weighs about 450 tonnes (450,000 kg) on the launch pad. It has a powerful cryogenic engine that uses liquid hydrogen and liquid oxygen as fuel. These pack in lots of energy in less volume and weight than the conventional solid or liquid propellants.

What are propellants?

Basically propellants are things which can be burnt easily to expel a hot gas which gives the force required to power the rocket. Burning requires both a burning material and an oxygen supply (which is crucial for burning), and both need to be present in a propellant mixture. It is also important that the propellant mixture does not have any unnecessary matter not connected with burning (specialists call these inert materials). There is a lot of advanced chemistry and chemical engineering involved in making propellants, and also a great deal of safety engineering.

Propellants all over the world are in either solid or liquid form in their natural state. Liquid propellants have more power packed into lesser weight of propellant mixture. In jet aircraft the propellant (refined kerosene) is burnt by oxygen taken from the atmosphere; but all launch vehicles and missiles have an oxidizer along with the propellant to provide the oxygen required to burn the fuel.

The common solid propellants in use are Carboxy Terminated Poly Butadine (CTPB) and Hydroxy Terminated Poly Butadine (HTPB). Both of these are solid polymers. They derive the oxygen for burning from the ammonium perchlorate which is mixed with them when they are cast in the rocket motor. Both propellants and the ammonium perchlorate are manufactured in India, based on technology developed by ISRO engineers. ISRO engineers have also developed a solid propellant similar to CTPB and HTPB based on castor oil. This was attempted as a standby option in the 1960s and 1970s when there were fears of advanced countries blocking some components of the standard solid propellants.

Liquid rockets can be made ready at any time, that is, you can pour propellants into rocket engines and keep them ready for launch. In the past aniline or kerosene were popular liquid propellants. The oxidizer used for these—kept separately in another tank—is Red Fuming Nitric Acid (RFNA).

Advanced earth storable liquid propellants are Unsymmetrical Dimethyl Mono Hydrazine (UDMH) and Mono Methyl Hydrazine (MMH). These two use Nitrogen Tetroxide (N_2O_4) as the oxidizer kept in a separate tank. India manufactures both UDMH and MMH. These are used for the PSLV and GSLV liquid stages.

A more advanced liquid engine is the semi-cryogenic one. While all the ones mentioned earlier use the propellant and oxidizer at room temperature, a semi-cryogenic engine uses the propellant (RP_1 or special kerosene) at room temperature and the oxidizer (LOX, liquid oxygen) which is at a very cold level.

The cryogenic engine has liquid hydrogen as fuel and liquid oxygen as oxidizer, both in a cryogenic or very cold state. This requires very advanced technology as in these super-cold conditions storage vessels, tubes, valves etc. require special materials and handling.

In the future nuclear materials might be used to propel a rocket.

While propellants are important, just burning them does not make a rocket fly to plan. There is a lot of science and technology involved in making these materials burn in an efficient manner to make a launch vehicle work. Even in a simple explosive like a firecracker, the more powerful the cracker, the more complex is its packing.

A jet aircraft engine has a lot in common with a rocket engine. However, there is a whole history of technological development in the area of propulsion which has led to the sophisticated design of launch vehicles and missiles. Propulsion addresses not only how the propellants are burned but also controls how they come out from the bottom of the rocket through nozzles. Since these burnings and gases involve high temperatures and strong chemicals there is a whole set of materials science and technology associated with propulsion. The weight of inert materials (that is non-burning materials) also needs to be kept to a minimum. Therefore a whole set of sciences, engineering and technology is required for excellent propulsion to take place.

Indian engineers mastered these technologies in the late 1960s. They tried them in rockets and later in SLV-3, subsequently improving them for the liquid engine called VIKAS used in PSLV. The engineers also built up the capability for ground testing of these rocket engines. These test facilities are situated at Sriharikota (now called Satish Dhawan Space Centre) and at Mahendragiri in Tamil Nadu.

How does one control a rocket?

The 'brain power' for directing and tilting the launch vehicle, raising it to the right orbit, detaching the used parts of launch vehicles (jettisoning), correcting deviations from expected pre-planned paths etc. are very important elements of a launch mission. Launch vehicles have many systems and subsystems to carry out these functions. Each of these is very complex in itself and involves key choices to be made by the launch vehicle designers.

Think for a moment of the problems involved in controlling and guiding a rocket so precisely that it can accurately place a satellite in orbit. When we drive on the road, we have road markers and the edge of the road to guide us, as also the landmarks on the way. For an aircraft in flight, the Air Traffic Controller (ATC) guides the pilot, in addition to the many guidance systems on board that the pilot has at his/her disposal and his/her own visuals.

But for a rocket, flying through the void of space, there are no landmarks. Of course the ground radars can 'see' the rocket, but they can only see it as a point in space. They cannot see how it is tilting—which is of crucial importance for the final positioning of the satellite. While an aircraft flies at a ground speed of about 800 km per hour, a rocket soon reaches 1 km per second, that is about 3,600 km per hour; at the time of injecting a satellite, it reaches a speed of about 7.5 km per second. The guidance for a rocket therefore has to be equally fast. It should also be able to act on the control system to effect necessary changes such as changing the tilt of the rocket or sending a command to jettison used parts. In the final phase of the mission, it has to sense whether the correct velocity has been attained and compute the right Delta V required for the satellite and the angle at which the final injection is to take place.

This means that the guidance system must be able to assess the position and the angle of the rocket in three dimensions, continuously and with great speed, while constantly measuring changes and making necessary adjustments.

Take a pencil in your hand. Hold it vertical. Now tilt it slowly away from you. This is called **pitching**—a movement that changes the angle away from the vertical. Now roll the pencil around slowly; this is called **rolling**. Move the pencil gently from left to right or from right to left, over a small angle. This is called **yaw**. These movements describe the exact ways in which a rocket is positioned.

One of the famous sensors that measures the yaw, pitch and roll of a rocket is the inertial sensor. The basic principle of this can be understood from a spinning top or lattu. When a top spins very fast, it holds itself vertical. Try to tilt it slightly, and it will come back to its vertical state. But even in the slightly tilted state, it will be firm and steady. This principle is what is used to measure the yaw, pitch and roll of a rocket, with sensors for all three dimensions. The 'spinning tops' are made of a very sophisticated material called beryllium. Advanced countries don't sell this as it has many strategic applications in the nuclear and military fields. India makes its own beryllium to meet its demands for inertial sensors: this is a joint venture of ISRO and the Bhabha Atomic Research Centre (BARC).

Making beryllium and machining it (it is very toxic and requires lots of safety precautions) are not enough to come up with an inertial sensor (called gyroscope or gyro). There are many calculations that have to be undertaken, a number of them involving physics and mathematics. India's development of inertial gyros started with the SLV-3 project. Though the initial space flights used French-made Inertial Measurement Units (IMUs), the subsequent ones had Indian-made gyros.

Inertial sensors can also be made of lasers—these are called laser gyros. India now has the capability to make these as well.

It is not enough to know the positions and angles of the rocket; one needs to be able to control them towards the desired direction. Small changes need to be continuously effected throughout the flight right till the injection of the satellite. This gentle controlling is done with the aid of a number of microthrusters placed in correctly calculated positions at different stages of the launch vehicle. Some microthrusters are kept even at the nozzle, directly deflecting the flame of gases. You will be amazed at how such very small thrusts of inert gases (almost like a cigarette puff) can change the direction of a mighty superspeed rocket in vital ways. Mind you, all rocket mission calculations depend on classical (applied) physics. There is no relativity, no quantum mechanics required, as the speeds are nowhere close to the speed of light and matter is dealt with at its gross levels—solids, liquids and gases. A lot of classical thermodynamics and fluid dynamics are applied to calculate rocket thrusts and to control microthrusters. Even the way the outer features of a rocket is designed takes into account several laws of aerodynamics so that the controls on the rocket flight can be effected smoothly. In some rockets the yaw–pitch–roll controls are effected through gentle movements of the rocket fins (no, these are not mere decorative pieces!).

The human aspect

When you start getting into the details of rocket design, you realize how much of basic mathematics, physics, chemistry, mechanical engineering, electronics, chemical engineering, metallurgy etc. interact in multiple ways towards a common purpose: the launch mission. For a mission like Chandrayaan-1 the science and mathematics of the movements of planets also enter into the equation in a major way.

The amount of knowledge and skills needed to make a rocket is mind-boggling. Add to that the designing of a satellite, which has a knowledge world of its own. But it is not just scientific and technical knowledge, computations and calculations and putting things together that is required in a space mission. Perhaps the most important aspect is the feelings and insights of the individuals involved in the mission.

Here is an episode that Dr Kalam recounted in his speech at the Satish Dhawan Space Centre in October 2003:

I remember another incident that happened during the third launch of SLV-3. The countdown sequence was proceeding smoothly. There were two operations to be carried out on the launcher—one for the release of the spacecraft umbilical and the other to release the arms holding the vehicle. Both these were pneumatically operated systems remotely controlled from Block House. The arms got released as expected. However the spacecraft umbilical release system failed to respond to the command. This held up the countdown automatically. There was suspense regarding how we should go about tackling the problem and the launch managers huddled together to find a solution. Shri M.R. Kurup and myself volunteered to reach the umbilical system through a ladder to manually release it. Seeing the situation, one young tradesman of SHAR, Shri Pappaiah, volunteered to climb on to the launcher and release the mechanism manually. After clearance by the concerned, he accomplished this marvellous feat and the vehicle was launched that day. I can never forget such committed individuals who have been the backbone of ISRO.

Such commitment is not displayed merely during the rocket launch which, naturally, gives everyone the peak of excitement. It is there throughout, from the first idea to the mission design, through experimentations and modifications, right till the final implementation. Churning out ideas, monitoring progress, anticipating problems and possible failure modes, schedule and budget controls—these are the constant concerns of every scientific, engineering, technical, administrative and finance personnel, of every member of the mission. It is a great human exercise in project management at the execution level, and in programme management at the overall ISRO level.

Where there is a large group of people there are always human emotions, both positive and negative. ISRO missions have seen their share of conflicts, petty jealousies and other human failures. Managing these complex human dilemmas in a humane way while keeping the overall programme goals in mind has been one of the great achievements of ISRO. ISRO personnel and their partners (small or big institutions or industries, state and central government agencies, as well as key individuals) have not only firmly launched India into space but also created a human cadre which can collectively focus complex multidimensional knowledge and skill bases towards accomplishing the most challenging missions.

Such commitment, and such managerial and leadership capabilities at different levels are crucial for several other daunting tasks that lie ahead for India.

Chapter 2

THE FUTURE OF SPACE EXPLORATION

In the previous chapter we talked at length about reaching outer space with the aid of rockets, and placing satellites in orbit. But we have not discussed how satellites are designed, built and used for various purposes. Satellites are built for a variety of missions: near-Earth scientific missions, planetary missions, remote sensing applications, communications, military applications, global position locations etc. While there are many principles common to the satellites built for these missions, each specific design has its own technological challenges and its own beauty. This is one of the reasons that space programmes continue to attract some of the best minds across the world.

Human presence in space—which started with Yuri Gagarin in 1960—is another area riven with great challenges. Though a lot has been achieved in the last fifty years, the truth is that we have barely scratched the surface of possibilities with our planetary and interplanetary missions.

We shall look at these areas in some detail soon, but let us first look broadly at the future of space exploration—what the scenario is likely to be over the next two to three decades. Where planning for the future is concerned, civilian and military applications will inevitably intertwine, as they do in other fields of human endeavour.

If we tried to cover the future of space programmes for the whole world, it would take several volumes. In this chapter we will focus only on projections for the Indian space programme.

This is what Dr Kalam had to say on the future of the Indian space programme at a symposium on 'Launch Vehicles: Past, Present and the Way Ahead' at Thiruvananthapuram on 28 July 2005. The symposium was held to celebrate the twenty-fifth anniversary of the successful launch of SLV-3.

_____

We constitute one-sixth of the world's population, and at least two-thirds of the global population today is going through the same crises and turmoils. Food, energy, water, health care, education and employment potential are important requirements for people to live with prosperity. The world at large needs technological inputs in order to meet these needs. Space technology has a role to play in this. Therefore, I am going to discuss with you the Vision for Space Missions, aimed at finding solutions to these requirements using space technology.

_____

Aerospace systems in India

India's space, missiles and aeronautics programmes in the last four decades have led to several successful missions and accomplishments. India is today self-reliant in space technology. It has evolved operational PSLV and GSLV which can provide competitive launch services. In the missile programme, India has operational strategic systems using critical technologies developed by indigenous efforts with multiple institutions partnership. The recent breakthrough has been BrahMos, a supersonic cruise missile, the best of its kind in the world attracting large-scale exports.

The vision of Dr Sarabhai and Prof. Satish Dhawan with two space profiles (1970–80 and 1980–95 respectively) were the blueprints, and today those visions have become reality. With these space profiles of our visionary leaders and with the integrated technology strength of the nation, we can march further to envision new missions.

Satellite applications

Though we get all excited about a Chandrayaan mission that lands a probe on the Moon or a mission that puts a human in space, we must remember that space programmes are not pursued solely for these moments of sensation. A much more worthy reason for pursuing a space programme is the immense benefit we derive from it in several walks of life. In fact, Vikram Sarabhai was attracted to the development of a space programme primarily because of the civilian benefits. As we have briefly seen before, a geostationary satellite like INSAT can reach all of India with equal coverage from Kashmir to Kanyakumari, and extending to the Andaman and Nicobar Islands and Lakshadweep Islands. Therefore telecommunications and television coverage can reach all of these regions. In times of disaster, if landlines or mobile towers are destroyed or submerged in water, transportable satellite terminals can be used to effect critical communications for relief operations.

The remote sensing of soils, forest cover, land, water etc. help in preservation of natural resources and also in planning their effective utilization. Ocean remote sensing helps fishermen to go to areas where fish are available in plenty. The remote sensing is based on the reflected and scattered rays of the optical spectrum and also on infra-red and microwave rays. Different objects reflect or scatter the rays differently, and in doing so they have their own unique 'signature'. Thus wheat will have one signature, and rice another. This difference can be detected by putting narrow filters in the camera (for red or blue or green or infra-red etc.) and determining what experts call the wavelength region. This data is then reconstructed on the ground from the digital signals (this is called image processing).

By comparing and contrasting different unique signatures, the objects on the Earth imaged by the satellite camera can be classified. If some rice fields are stressed by water shortage or pests, they will be seen differently from healthy crops. Degraded soils and healthy soils can be classified too, so that effective measures can be taken to make them better. So also polluted and clean water bodies can be identified and the spread of pollution can be charted. There are many such applications. India is considered to be a leader in remote sensing applications. Almost every state in India has a Remote Sensing Centre in addition to remote sensing applications technology being absorbed by almost all traditional agencies in India, be it for agriculture, forestry, water resources or zoology.*

Y.S. Rajan was one of the early pioneers in the spread of remote sensing applications in India. The founders of remote sensing in India were the late Prof. P.R. Pisharty and Prof. P.D. Bhavsar. There are many more pioneers in their respective areas of applications and also in developing new forms of image processing technologies. D.S. Kamat laid the foundation for image processing in ISRO and Dr George Joseph for building satellite borne remote sensing cameras.

In his vision for the future speech, Dr Kalam rightly started from a very brief description of benefits from the Indian space programme. To quote again from his address:

---

*The National Remote Sensing Centre (NRSC) has placed on a portal the full information on the status of natural resources in India. You can see it on its website: www.nrsc.gov.in and on http://applications.nrsc.gov.in15001/ Bhoosampada. Other useful networks for remote sensing applications are: http://www.irs-nrsc.gov.in/index.php, http://www.ibin.co.in (Indian Bioresource Information Network), http://www.bisindia.org (Biodiversity Information System), www.sac.gov.in and http://www.nosdac.gov.in (Meteorological and Oceanographic Satellite Data Analysis Centre). You can go down to details around the district, taluk and village of your interest. It is the power of satellite remote sensing coupled with the Geographic Information System (GIS) that allows you to zoom in.

Satellite remote sensing

Satellite remote sensing is vital for mapping of different ground resources like water, minerals, agriculture, urban planning, coastal regions, forestry, engineering geology and mineral exploration. Regional research centres in the many states/ regions of our country and multiple villages are utilizing the data coming from the satellites. This large potential must be effectively used.

Disaster management

In many places on our planet, we experience severe disasters like earthquakes, tsunamis, cyclones resulting in loss of life and loss of wealth—and in some cases a natural calamity destroys the decades of progress made by a country and its valuable civilizational heritage. India has earthquake problems periodically in certain regions. The US, Japan, Turkey, Iran and many other countries also suffer due to earthquakes.

Earthquakes and tsunamis are sub-terraineous phenomena and predicting these from space observations would be a great challenge. Space scientists of multiple nations should work with determination to use deep penetration satellite images to predict an earthquake or shock wave propagation. Other possibilities are the precise geodynamic measurement of strain accumulation by satellite to detect pre-slip, and of electromagnetic phenomena prior to final rupture.

It is hoped that well-organized electromagnetic monitoring may provide unique observational information on the pre-slips. Atmospheric/ionospheric anomalies still remain unresolved. Post-earthquake disaster recovery, communication and damage assessment are also areas where space technology can quickly make its impact. We have to mount research programmes for evolving a systematic methodology for determining the effects leading to earthquakes and tsunamis. Space technology can be used for forecasting and modelling of volcanic eruptions, landslides, avalanches, flash floods, storm surges, hurricanes and tornadoes. We should also integrate the various efforts with the National Authority for Disaster Management.

Communication networks

The satellite communication network has helped India in providing education and health care in the form of tele-education and tele-medicine. The prime objective of the EDUSAT programme is to provide support to education through low-cost ground segments and to reach the unreached people of India in every nook and corner. EDUSAT is specially configured to have multiple beams covering different regions of India. EDUSAT provides communication coverage through five regional beams and a national beam. This system will be primarily for school, college and higher level of education; however, it will also support non-formal education. EDUSAT is expected to provide 150,000 ground terminals in its full capacity.

Like tele-education, tele-medicine can help in a big way in bringing modern health care treatment within the reach of remote villages. I am happy to know that ISRO has used satellite networks to connect remote villages to major hospitals wherein a patient's condition is diagnosed by a specialist doctor and his views communicated through the communication links.

These links would be the window to the world of knowledge for our villages and also reap the benefits of our e-governance, tele-education, tele-medicine, e-commerce and e-judiciary initiatives. I visualize establishment of village knowledge centres in all Panchayats to empower the villagers with the knowledge and to act as a nodal centre for knowledge connectivity for the villagers. The knowledge centre will provide to the villagers real-time information about market details on their products from the agriculture, cottage industry, fisheries and other rural industries in their locality as well as national markets. This will also provide direct quality employment to over one million people who will be instrumental in promoting a higher level of wealth generation in our rural sector.

The technology base built up so far

Before projecting for the future, one should address one's own capabilities, strengths and weaknesses. When the Indian space programme was conceived during the 1960s, the USSR and the USA were engaged in massive competitive space programmes of their own, both in the civilian and military fields. Manned space missions were already a reality. The geosynchronous satellite launch and its applications had been demonstrated, though in a rudimentary manner. The manned mission to the Moon had been announced by the USA and work on the Apollo series had started. Indian scientists and engineers were fully aware of these developments. However, India did not start with a GSLV project.

If one assessed India's technological capability in the 1960s (of universities, national laboratories including ISRO and BARC, and industries in the public and private sectors), we were just starting off in advancements in mechanical, electrical, chemical, metallurgical and electronics engineering. We were nowhere near the USSR or the USA or the developed European nations. So the three major projects selected by India as the first for its space programme were quite ambitious, though they were relatively simple by the standards of the USSR and the USA at the time.

The Indian space programme started with these three projects:

1. The use of an American satellite called Application Technology Satellite (ATS-6) for conducting Satellite Instructional Experiment in India (SITE). India's major role was to develop the ground system including a number of receiving stations in villages and to produce the instructional materials.

2. The construction of the first Indian satellite Aryabhata to be

launched by the Soviet launch vehicle Intercosmos from the USSR. While the design of Aryabhata was done by the Indian team, some elements of structure, batteries and solar arrays were obtained free of charge from the Soviets. The ground system to track the satellite was built by the Indian team. Even one in the USSR, near Moscow, was established by the Indian engineers.

3. The launch of a 50 kg near-Earth orbit satellite with a satellite launch vehicle designed and made in India. This third project was technologically the most challenging. The SITE experiment was conducted during 1975–76 and Aryabhata was launched in 1975, but the SLV project took more time and the first successful launch, with SLV-3 putting Rohini in orbit, was in 1980.

In addition, around the same time, ISRO started building up technological and applications strengths in many areas of space and ground systems. Remote sensing started with aircraft surveys and also with the receiving of remote sensing pictures (image data) from the USA's LANDSAT satellite. Many major ground test facilities were constructed. A strong liquid engine programme was launched with French participation during the 1970s itself, without waiting for the SLV-3 launch.

The beginning in all these areas was made after assessing the available and projected strengths. It has now been proven that the choices made then were good and have put India on a solid path of progress in space science, technology and applications.

It is similarly necessary to assess the current strengths when planning the way forward for the Indian space programme. Let us look at Dr Kalam's thoughts on the matter, from the same talk as before.

Aerospace technology strength

Due to various aerospace programmes, multiple state-of-the-art technologies were developed. Computational Fluid Dynamics (CFD) emerged as a core strength for India with advanced software codes and supercomputing capability to optimize configurations for guided missiles, LCA and launch vehicles. CAD/CAM have become the order of the day for aerospace systems and virtual reality systems have been developed which reduce the design and product realization time by as much as 40 per cent. India has developed fibre-optic and ring laser gyros with better accuracy; microprocessors, microwave components and devices, phase shifters, onboard computers and foundries for making VLSI and MMIC components have also been set up, making India self-dependent. In the area of propulsion, ISRO's large solid propulsion booster giving 500 tonnes of thrust, liquid propulsion in DRDO and ISRO, and the development effort of cryogenic engines established a sound base in propulsion technology.

Emerging aerospace technologies

Emerging technologies such as micro-electromechanical systems (MEMS), nanotechnology, information technology, biotechnology, space research, hypersonics and high power lasers and microwaves will be dominating the future in every field and applications. The advancements in material science and technology will give a major thrust to the realization of advanced aerospace systems. We are today at the convergence of nano-, bio- and information technologies, which will lead to new generation aerospace devices and products.

MEMS and nanotechnology

The advances in the fields of micro-electromechanical systems (MEMS) and nanotechnology have paved the way for the ability to manufacture smaller and smarter products. MEMS bring together microelectronics with micromachining technology, allowing unprecedented levels of functionality and reliability to be placed on a small silicon chip. Nanotechnology, on the other hand, is the science of assembling atoms and molecules that respond to stimuli, with dimensions on the order of a nanometre (one billionth of a metre).

MEMS devices for aerospace application

MEMS technology will have a profound impact in the aerospace field with the miniaturization of electronics. These tiny machines, often only a few micrometres in size, are already replacing conventional larger equipment. Given their microscopic size and weight, MEMS can use higher frequency and bandwidths and can be slipped into tighter and more environmentally stressed locations. Once in production, their unit prices are lower; once in operation, the power consumption is negligible. Examples of MEMS are to be found in pressure sensors, fluid flow sensors, magnetic sensors, gyros, accelerometers and more. MEMS is also expected to play a significant role in dramatically reducing the cost of space exploration with substantial savings in weight and increased reliability and functionality. Eventually, MEMS could lead to the development of extremely low cost micro-satellites.

Nanotechnology

Molecular nanotechnology has enormous potential for future aerospace systems. Research has shown that newly discovered classes of molecules, particularly carbon nano tubes built from graphite sheets curved into a wide variety of closed shapes, may lead to tougher, high-temperature materials that can survive in vacuum and other harsh environments. Carbon nano tubes are a normal form of carbon with remarkable electrical and mechanical properties. It is hoped that such materials could revolutionize electronic design and open the space frontier by radically lowering the cost of launch to orbit.

Carbon nano tubes reinforced with a polymer matrix will result in composites which are super-strong, lightweight, small and intelligent structures in the field of material science. This has tremendous aerospace applications. Molecular switches and circuits along with nano cells will pave the way for the next generation computers. Ultra-dense computer memory coupled with excellent electrical performance will result in low-power, low-cost, nano size and yet faster assemblies.

The Indian space programme and its impact on the economy

As long as things are done on a small scale, one can afford to assess them purely on the technical strengths and capabilities of individuals desiring to implement them. But large-scale projects and programmes requiring large funds from public sources (that is, taxpayers' money) need more careful scrutiny. The return on investment for such programmes need not necessarily be assessed as the profit generated by the projects. The questions to be asked are: Do they generate downstream industry and, through them, large-scale employment? Do they generate as spin-offs technological capabilities which may create many new business opportunities?

For example, NASA has to show one example (amongst many) of the material called Teflon which emerged from space research and has created a revolution in applications: from the chemical industry to electronic cables and wires to non-stick pans used in many households. Similarly, image processing technology, mainly developed for space, has led to a revolution in printing technology, as also the solar photovoltaic technology developed to power satellites. Nickel cadmium batteries are now used to power wristwatches and many miniature electronic devices. Titanium, the wonder metal, and several composites had their growth through the space programme as well.

Of course, the Indian space programme cannot claim these achievements for itself as its own inventions. ISRO has taken many ideas and inventions from the world. But the development of subsystems and components are done to ISRO specifications or as per ISRO designs. Such tasks have made many Indian industries (big, medium and small) upgrade their technological strengths, which help them in their own production lines in terms of overall improvement of quality and performance of their regular products. About 500 such Indian industries participate in ISRO and DRDO projects and programmes as subcontractors. In addition there are many downstream industries (like those which use the space segment, mainly satellites, to provide socially and economically useful services and products) which are successful commercial entities. DTH (Direct to Home) TV distribution companies come under this category—and this is a fast-growing business with the promise of large-scale employment.

Indian industries are emerging stronger as a result of advances in the space programme. ISRO's commercial arm ANTRIX has many Indian and foreign orders. Recently, the Confederation of Indian Industry (CII) held a first-ever industry-driven International Space Exhibition and Seminar at Bengaluru. It was named Bengaluru Space Expo 2008 and is likely to be repeated in 2010. Thus space-based businesses are growing in India and are likely to become an important percentage of the Indian GDP, as they are in developed countries like the USA, Russia, France, Germany etc.

Dr Kalam looks far ahead in terms of future possibilities in this area in his speech delivered on 28 July 2005.

Having missed the opportunity of the first industrial revolution, India is still a developing country. Now the developed countries are racing towards the Moon and Mars, which may be the next industrial revolution. India has the opportunity now to join this exclusive club of nations to establish industries on the Moon and Mars. The technological challenges are:

- Manufacturing and mining in reduced gravity
- Harnessing Helium-3 on the Moon for future energy, using oncoming fusion technologies
- Using dry ice deposits on the Moon and Mars as sources of fuel for rocket engines
- Extending the life of satellites in orbit through refuelling and repairing
- Using the Moon as a space transportation hub.

Cost of access to space

As space missions are increasing in frequency with ever-larger payloads, it is essential to reduce the cost of access to space by several orders of magnitude. Such a reduction can enable the global space community to move out of the present era of information collection missions into an era of mass movement missions. They can find solutions for the energy, water and mineral crisis. Mankind will continue to live on Earth for many billion years. We need a good life for our future generations. Therefore, it is necessary to bring resources the Earth needs from other planets.

Future space missions

In his speech, Dr Kalam emphasizes the need for multiple uses of the same satellite by extending its life in orbit, and of low-cost access to space. These two capabilities—which in themselves contain the need for the creation of a new and complex set of technologies—will lead to space services that offer competitive advantages many times more than the simple extrapolation of currently existing methods.

What Dr Kalam has outlined are within the realms of possibility; however, many detailed studies and assessments are needed before his vision can become a reality. The assessments would not be purely technological but would include assessments of alternate options to meet the end goals with less costs and lesser risks. ISRO's scientists, engineers and policymakers will undertake these studies and assessments in the coming years. In addition ISRO has before it the challenge of executing its first human launch mission within a decade.

Let us look at some other ideas that are part of Dr Kalam's vision for the future:

Integrated aerospace technology strength would lead to better capacity utilization, and the creation of low-cost space transportation. We have to evolve innovative design concepts for small as well as large payloads. Both single- and two-stage to orbit RLV concepts can be examined. The goal here is to reduce the cost of access to space by one to two orders of magnitude. Even a scientific breakthrough, for example, in air-breathing propulsion system may lead to a space transportation revolution. The world space community has a huge stake in such breakthrough research in advanced inter-disciplinary and inter-institutional collaboration. A concerted effort is thus needed to quickly demonstrate the technology for low-cost access to space. ISRO must take the lead in bringing the space community together.

Reusable aerospace vehicles

The global space industry has had a forty-year period of unprecedented growth and prosperity. The geostationary orbit is nearly full, and new Earth orbits need study and exploration, especially the use of small satellites in equatorial low-Earth orbit. Currently, the global space industry has a capacity to launch over 200 tonnes of satellites every year. However, the forecast is that projected demand will consume less than half of this established capacity. Thus a bitter price war is on to capture this limited market.

The Indian concept of the hyperplane, a fully reusable system, is an innovation in rocketry providing a payload fraction of 15 per cent, drastically reducing the launch cost. The concept of mass addition in space has been appreciated worldwide and a few countries have started working on the heat exchanger for on-board generation of liquid oxygen. There is an urgent need to progress the cost effective SSTO hypersonic plane in our country.

Aerospace system applications: A perspective

With the growing space efforts, the coming years will have a dominance of reusable launch vehicles. They will provide cost-effective transportation of heavy payloads in order to construct large structures in space. The future needs will be solar power satellites for generation of electric power, exploration of planets, mining on the Moon and Mars and in space habitats.

Space missions 2005–30

In the last twenty-five years, Indian space, missile and aircraft technologies have matured and now have a tremendous integrated potential for developing world class newer systems. While we are celebrating this silver jubilee, we must look forward to missions for the next twenty-five years. Therefore, I suggest the following space missions:

- Manned space missions to the Moon and Mars and the establishment of space industries
- Cost-effective space transportation systems using hypersonic reusable vehicles (SSTO)
- Harnessing space energy for generating power and drinking water

- Developing solar sail for interplanetary missions
- Integrated disaster management system utilizing space technology
- Refuelling, repair and maintenance of satellites in geo orbit
- Operational Indian navigational satellites.

Future space missions throw open new opportunities and challenges to the scientific community and the youth of India. Use this opportunity to make the nation great.

The space missions and programmes mentioned by Dr Kalam are broad-brush paintings on a big canvas. They are meant to ignite the minds of those who are willing to dare, as Vikram Sarabhai and the team of ISRO pioneers dared in the 1960s. There are other ideas, merely hinted at above, that one can imagine further. India and a few other countries may partner to build a new type of space station that can combine many operational facilities currently being performed by individual satellites. There are also possibilities of having many small satellites carry out one or two specific tasks (e.g. tracking ship movements). India could also be an important part of a worldwide exploration of planetary systems and of our galaxy. The possibilities of space have not yet been exhausted. This is an area that will continue to challenge bright minds not only during the twenty-first century but much beyond.

We have not talked so far about the military uses of space and the question of security in space, the danger of space debris etc. (You might have read about two satellites, one Russian and the other American, that collided in 2009.) We will devote the last chapter in this section to military applications and space security, starting off with an overview of India's applications capability extracted from a recent ISRO report.

Chapter 3

EVOLVING SPACE TECHNOLOGIES

As you might expect, all major funding by the government or by private sources depend upon the benefits of the application that is being funded. The aim of the private sector is the eventual profit (return on investment) that is likely to be made from the present investment. Government funding need not always be aimed at immediate or short-term gains from the investment; more often, its goal is the overall growth of the economy, the generation of new employment or the enhancement of the public good such as national security or national prestige. Economic growth and employment generation are measurable, considering the benefits or profits generated by a programme for other industries, downstream businesses and also in terms of savings made in existing operations.

For example, satellite communication speeds up access to a point where there are better profits all around. It also enables access to remote areas, which opens up new avenues of employment and profit, and has a public good component as well. Satellite communication has also generated many downstream industries like direct-to-home television (DTH), position location etc., creating new businesses and employment, and therefore new taxes and more economic growth. Civilian remote-sensing applications are another example of a profitable and growth-oriented sector.

The economics of the Indian space programme have been studied by a number of researchers. Y.S. Rajan, S. Chandrasekhar and Gopal Raj did one of the earliest quantitative studies in the area. If you look at the larger picture, the cost-to-benefit ratio from the Indian space programme is very attractive in the national context. Individual industries that pick up some specific elements from the space programme for their business also make handsome profits. However, the government has to continue to play a major part in supporting ISRO to create new technologies and demonstrate new applications. The overall wealth creation in the country through the space programme justifies such an investment by the government of the taxpayers' money. One of the reasons for this positive impact is that the Indian space programme is implemented very effectively with strict consideration of project management principles. In fact if some of the project management methodologies of ISRO were followed in other public and private sector projects, India would gain a lot in terms of better and more regulated returns from the funds invested. This 'soft' benefit itself is a great achievement of ISRO and it has not yet been fully utilized by our country.

In his speeches Dr Kalam refers very often to these sound programme management principles: vision, mission, targets, leadership at various levels, the ability to manage failures and learning from them, keeping the team motivated, and above all the continuous generation of new ideas, new projects, new capabilities and the ability to respond to the changing world.

A brief profile of ISRO

ISRO is one of the organizations which as a matter of policy believes in large-scale dissemination of information to the public. Some extracts from the annual report for 2008 gives a glimpse into its technological capability and its application infrastructure build up so far.

The Indian space programme witnessed several major successes and reached great heights during the year by successfully orbiting an unmanned spacecraft Chandrayaan-1 around the Moon, launching ten satellites in a single launch, conducting the acceptance test of an indigenously developed cryogenic engine successfully and launching a commercial satellite for an international customer. India achieved a rare feat in its space endeavours at 20.31 hrs on 14 November 2008 by placing the Indian tricolour on the Moon when the Moon Impact Probe (MIP), one of the payloads on Chandrayaan-1, hit the lunar surface; it joined a select band of countries who have placed an object on the Moon.

PSLV-C9/CARTOSAT-2A/IMS-1 missions

ISRO created a record on 28 April 2008 by successfully launching Polar Satellite Launch Vehicle PSLV-C9 placing ten satellites, viz., CARTOSAT-2A, Indian Mini Satellite (IMS-1) and eight nanosatellites from abroad into orbit.

The Polar Satellite Launch Vehicle with thirteen consecutively successful flights so far has repeatedly proved itself as a reliable and versatile workhorse launch vehicle. It has demonstrated multiple satellite launch capability, having launched a total of sixteen satellites for international customers besides fourteen Indian payloads including Chandrayaan-1 and satellites for remote sensing, amateur radio communications and the Space Capsule Recovery Experiment (SRE-1). PSLV was used to launch ISRO's exclusive meteorological satellite Kalpana-1 into a Geosynchronous Transfer Orbit (GTO) in September 2002 and thus proved its versatility.

CARTOSAT-2A, launched on 28 April 2008, is a state-of-the-art 690 kg remote sensing satellite with a spatial resolution of about one metre and a swath of 9.6 km. The satellite carries a panchromatic camera (PAN) capable of taking black-and-white pictures in the visible region of the electromagnetic spectrum. The highly agile CARTOSAT-2A is steerable along as well as across the direction of its movement to facilitate imaging of any area more frequently. High-resolution data from CARTOSAT-2A will be invaluable in urban and rural development applications calling for large-scale mapping. The PAN camera onboard CARTOSAT-2A has started beaming high-quality imagery of India and other parts of the globe.

Indian Mini Satellite (IMS-1), flown as an auxiliary payload on board PSLV-C9, is developed by ISRO for remote sensing applications. Weighing 83 kg at lift-off, IMS-1 incorporates many new technologies and has miniaturized subsystems. IMS-1 carries two remote sensing payloads: a multi-spectral camera (Mx payload) and a hyper-spectral camera (HySI payload), operating in the visible and near infrared regions of the electromagnetic spectrum. The data from this mission will be made available to interested space agencies and the student community from developing countries to provide the necessary impetus to capacity building in using satellite data. The cameras onboard the versatile IMS-1 have been providing high quality imagery.

The Indian National Satellite (INSAT) system

Having established the need for a domestic communication satellite through the Satellite Instructional Television Experiment (SITE) using the ATS-6 satellite of USA during 1975–76, the Satellite Telecommunication Experimental Project (STEP) using the Franco–German satellite Symphonie in 1978–79 and by building and utilizing the experimental communication satellite APPLE, the Indian National Satellite (INSAT-1) system was operationalized in 1983. INSAT-1 satellites procured from abroad were multipurpose satellites providing telecommunication, TV broadcasting and meteorological services. INSAT-2, -3, -4 and GSAT satellites, designed indigenously with higher power, more weight and the capability to provide various services have been built and operationalized. India today has one of the largest domestic communications satellite systems in the Asia Pacific region with eleven operational satellites in orbit with more than 210 transponders providing vital services to the country.

The meteorological data from the INSAT system is used for quick dissemination of warnings against impending disasters from approaching cyclones; specially designed receivers have been installed at vulnerable coastal areas in the country for direct transmission of warnings to the officials and public using the INSAT broadcast capability.

EDUSAT, a satellite dedicated to providing educational services, was launched in September 2004. EDUSAT is providing a wide range of educational delivery modes like one-way TV broadcast, interactive

TV, video conferencing, computer conferencing, web-based instructions etc. About 34,000 classrooms utilizing EDUSAT covering twenty-three states have been set up across the country. These network connections have been set up at different schools, colleges, training institutes and other departments.

Telemedicine is another important initiative to use space technology for societal benefits. It has enabled the population, even in the remotest parts, to have access to super-specialty medical care. At present, the telemedicine network of ISRO has more than 330 installations of which about forty-five are super-specialty hospitals and ten are mobile units. Till now, more than 300,000 patients have benefited annually from the telemedicine system. Plans are underway to extend telemedicine benefits to all parts of the country.

The Indian Remote Sensing (IRS) satellite system

Using remote sensing satellites for Earth observation was initiated with the design and development of the experimental remote sensing satellites Bhaskara-1 and Bhaskara-2 during the mid-70s. With seven satellites—IRS-1D, OCEANSAT-1, Technology Experiment Satellite (TES), RESOURCESAT-1, CARTOSAT-1, CARTOSAT-2 and CARTOSAT-2A—now in operation, the Indian Remote Sensing satellite system is the largest civilian remote sensing satellite constellation in the world and provides imageries in a variety of spatial resolutions from better than one metre (CARTOSAT-2 and -2A) to 188 metres (IRS-1D). Forthcoming satellites include OCEANSAT-2, RESOURCESAT-2 and a new radar imaging satellite, RISAT, that can overcome the present limitation of imaging under cloudy conditions.

Using the data from IRS satellites, a variety of application programmes such as groundwater prospects mapping, crop acreage and production estimation, potential fishing zone forecast, biodiversity characterization at a landscape level, covering the four main biodiversity-rich regions of the country—the North-East, the Western Himalayas, the Western Ghats and Andaman and Nicobar Islands—have been operationalized.

In order to reach space-based services directly to the rural population, Village Resource Centres (VRCs) were launched in 2004. VRCs provide a variety of space-based products and services including tele-education, telemedicine and information on natural resources. So far, nearly 400 VRCs have been set up in association with NGOs/ Trusts, institutes and government agencies.

Satellite launch vehicles

From launching of modest-sounding rockets in the 1960s, India has now acquired the capability to launch remote sensing satellites using the Polar Satellite Launch Vehicle (PSLV) and geosynchronous communication satellites using GSLV. PSLV is capable of launching a 1.5 tonne satellite into polar sun-synchronous orbit. Geosynchronous Satellite Launch Vehicle (GSLV) can launch a 2 to 2.5 tonne satellite into geostationary transfer orbit (GTO). GSLV has four successful flights out of five missions with the last one being the GSLV-F04/ INSAT-4CR mission on 2 September 2007. Development of an indigenous cryogenic stage to replace the presently used Russian cryogenic stage has been successfully realized. The flight acceptance test of the cryogenic engine was conducted successfully on 18 December 2008.

GSLV-Mk III, which is under development, will be capable of launching satellites weighing 4 tonnes into GTO. Several developments including recoverable and reusable space transportation systems are in progress with the objective of reducing the cost of access to space.

Commercial successes

Antrix, the commercial arm of the Department of Space, is a single window agency for marketing Indian space capabilities. It is playing a key role in the worldwide availability of IRS data through Geoeye, USA. Antrix also provides IRS data processing equipment. Antrix offers launch services using India's PSLV. So far sixteen satellites have been successfully launched by PSLV for various international customers. Through Antrix, telemetry, tracking and command support from Indian ground stations are offered to various satellite operators. Similarly, lease of transponders from the INSAT system has been made possible. In this regard, eleven transponders have already been leased to INTELSAT. Customers for the spacecraft components offered by Antrix include the world's leading spacecraft manufacturers. The W2M satellite built by ISRO/Antrix under an agreement entered into with EADS Astrium, Paris was launched successfully on 20 December 2008. Besides, Antrix has won contracts from Europe and Asia for launch services in the highly competitive international launch services market. After the successful development of a low cost, compact, modular and rugged Automatic Weather Station (AWS), the technology has been licensed to industry for regular production. Thus, in addition to successfully developing spacecraft and launch vehicle technologies indigenously, India has also been successful in the application of satellite technology to benefit its national economy. At the same time, India has also been sharing space-based information with the international community and providing commercial space services globally.

Military applications

The technological capabilities of ISRO's programmes also embed in them many military application capabilities. One cannot calculate return-on-investment for military, defence and security aspects—they are required for any country. But policymakers and practitioners definitely do make another kind of calculation before funding a defence or military project. This has to do with determining what the most cost-effective way of doing a task is, given the end requirements or needs, and given the options available.

Military applications of space have to go through this exercise as well. Studies and discussions have gone on since the 1970s on the use of space technologies for the Indian defence forces. While ISRO's space programme was sharply tuned to the needs of civilian applications and the study of space sciences, ISRO engineers were fully aware of the military applications of space, not just in terms of missiles but also through satellite communications, remote sensing (surveillance) and meteorology, position location, cartography etc. Many of the ISRO's launch vehicles, satellites and ground systems have embedded in them elements of technologies and systems that can be easily and effectively transformed to military applications.

That is why most space technologies in the world come under the area of Dual Use Technologies (that is, both civilian and military use) and are generally not shared by advanced countries with developing countries. India was also denied many critical technologies. But once Indian engineers proved their capabilities, the imports became liberal!

Let us look at the military applications of space in India.

The missile force

When one thinks of military applications that have to do with space, the first thing that comes to mind are missiles. Why must we develop missiles? While alternate methods of delivery such as superfast aircraft like F-16s or Sukhois have their roles in military strategy, many situations demand the unmanned high-speed delivery of a warhead to a narrow target. This is where a missile is ideal. A guided missile can be used for short distances and also very long distances (over even 2,000 km or more), with very high accuracies (within metres).

With a nuclear warhead, the availability of missile becomes essential. Of course, nuclear weapons are meant to play the role of a deterrent in warfare. But a deterrent should be in a fully ready condition and in an operational mode, capable of being dispatched at once. That is what a missile is capable of.

India started in a major way on the Integrated Guided Missile development programme in 1982, when Dr Kalam joined the Defence Research and Development Organization (DRDO) after leaving ISRO. His ISRO experience, as also the capabilities built in many industries and institutions through the implementation of the SLV-3 project, was a great asset to the missile development programme at DRDO. Before the arrival of Dr Kalam, DRDO scientists and engineers had also built up a number of capabilities essential to missile building. Prithvi, the surface-to-surface missile developed by DRDO, is now operationally used by the Indian Army on a large scale. The intercontinental ballistic missile (ICBM) Agni, capable of long distance nuclear weapon delivery, has also been commissioned. Other missiles are under induction trials. In addition to these, Indian defence forces induct foreign missiles selectively to meet specific requirements.

The supersonic cruise missile BrahMos is the latest addition to the arsenal. BrahMos, which is a joint venture between India and Russia—its name is derived from a merging of the names of the rivers Brahmaputra and Moskva—has several firsts to its credit in its performance at the world level. It can be fitted into ships, submarines and also fighter aircrafts. It can travel speedier than sound and cruise at high speeds just above the stratosphere to avoid easy detection. In terms of accuracy, it can target a specific building that it is directed towards. And this accuracy is achieved not through continuous command and control but by a pre-programming done at the time of the launch. That is the extent of the intelligence built into the onboard control and guidance system of the BrahMos.

This is what Dr Kalam has to say about BrahMos.

Fusion of the core competence of two nations

Let me share with you a unique experience of developing a complex system through a joint venture using the core competence of two nations. The technological and managerial cooperation of the two nations and an investment of around $200 million by each nation have enabled the realization of the first supersonic cruise missile called BrahMos within five years. The foundation of the joint venture is based on joint design, development, production and marketing. One of the significant technological breakthroughs of this decade is the design, development and productionization of BrahMos by an Indo–Russian joint venture.

BrahMos is the first supersonic operational cruise missile in the world, which can be launched from multiple platforms such as ships, submarines, road mobiles and silos, and with modifications from aircraft. This technological innovation is a trendsetter in the cruise missile field. The robust design of the missile, elaborate ground tests and simulation have ensured a 100 per cent success rate in all the flight tests conducted for the Armed Forces by the joint venture company. In successful design, development, production and marketing of the BrahMos missile, an innovative way of technology cooperation has emerged between India and other countries for multi-billion dollar business.

How does a missile work?

A missile is basically a rocket. It follows the same principles of physics and engineering conditions discussed for launch vehicles. It has a similar control system for controlling pitch, roll and yaw and for position location. But a missile goes further up in a near-vertical position, clearing the troposphere very fast. It is directed upwards with a little tilt, so that it can follow a near parabolic path in space and go a long distance away from the place of launch.

The technological complexity of a missile mission, and its main difference with a satellite launch mission, lies in the fact that a missile has to return to Earth to hit the intended target. When it returns towards the Earth, the missile has to travel through the dense atmosphere at a very high speed. It has to deal with the resultant friction without burning out like the spent or jettisoned parts of a satellite launch vehicle or a meteorite. It has to remain intact and keep its payload—which is a warhead, a nuclear bomb or other high-capacity bombs—safe. It then needs to reach its designated target on the ground accurately, and land the warhead. That is what makes missile technology much more difficult than what is needed to develop satellite launch vehicles.

The final targeting phase is the most crucial part of a missile mission. The missile has to map the terrain accurately and hit the right target. Sophisticated missiles like BrahMos have a lot of manoeuvring capability at the terminal phases, to avoid detection by the enemy. These technologies are important for missiles to be effective in warfare.

On the other hand, re-entry calls for a completely different technology that is not used in civilian SLV programmes except for space shuttles that have to be brought back to Earth for reuse along with their human passengers. The amount of heat generated by friction is enormous. If we rub our hands together for a sufficiently long time, we can even get blisters. You can imagine the kind of heat that is generated by the atmosphere when a speedy object penetrates it.

What is done to overcome the heat of friction on re-entry for a missile? If you look at a rocket or a missile, you will see that it has a cone-like structure at the top: some may be sharp, some more rounded and bulbous. This is called a nosecone. It has two roles: to penetrate the atmosphere with least resistance, according to the laws of fluid dynamics; and to protect the payload carried by the rocket from the harsh friction of the atmosphere.

In a scientific rocket, the nosecone opens once the rocket is in outer space, allowing the scientific instruments to conduct their experiment. In a satellite mission such as Chandrayaan-1, the nosecone opens before injecting the satellite into its orbit, thus protecting the satellite during the rough passage through the dense atmosphere.

In a missile the payload (warhead) has to be protected both times, first when travelling upwards through the atmosphere, and during re-entry. During re-entry, the payload can get very hot because the missile has acquired a very high speed by then (unlike during lift-off). If metals or fibreglass are used in a missile as in sounding rockets and satellite launching missions, they may burn or get so very hot that they melt, or the warhead inside may explode.

So, missile technologies resort to a trick, using nature's law. The surface of the nosecone and the tip are made of carbon—an element that burns easily with heat! The trick is not to use carbon in the pure form. Through the technology of composite materials several small threads of carbon are interwoven in an extremely compressed form (carbon–carbon composites) and the tip that bears the brunt of penetration is made of a carbon–carbon block. Such materials do not conduct heat. Therefore the heat is absorbed, with the top layer of the nosecone becoming very hot and burning at the surface. The top surface has to face a temperature of about 4000–4500°K (-273°C). The inside remains cool! There is sufficient material on the nose-tip and the rest of the nosecone that atmospheric friction cannot burn through them till the missile reaches its target.

Dr Kalam spoke about re-entry technology in an address during the Technology Day awards function at New Delhi on 11 May 2007.

On 10 January 2007, the country witnessed in real time the flight of PSLV-C7 from Satish Dhawan Space Centre, SHAR, Sriharikota, successfully placing four satellites—India's CARTOSAT-2 and Space Capsule Recovery Experiment (SRE-1), Indonesia's LAPAN-TUBSAT and Argentina's PEHUENSAT-1—into a 635 km polar orbit.

Recovery of Space Capsule Recovery Experiment (SRE-1), a major technological feat

SRE-1 was successfully recovered on 22 January 2007, after being manoeuvred to re-enter the Earth's atmosphere and descend over Bay of Bengal about 140 km east of Sriharikota. The critical manoeuvres were executed from the Spacecraft Control Centre (SCC) of ISRO at Bangalore supported by a network of ground stations in India and abroad.

On 22 January, the re-orientation of the SRE-1 capsule for de-boost operations commenced at 08.42 a.m. (IST). The capsule made its re-entry at 09.37 a.m. at an altitude of 100 km with a velocity of 8 km/sec (29,000 km per hour). During its re-entry, the capsule was protected from the intense heat by carbon phenolic ablative material and silica tiles on its outer surface. SRE-1 splashed down in the Bay of Bengal with a velocity of 12 m/sec (about 43 km per hour) at 09.46 a.m. The flotation system, which immediately got triggered, kept the capsule floating. Recovery operations were supported and carried out by the Indian Coast Guard and Indian Navy using ships, aircraft and helicopters. During its stay in orbit for twelve days, two experiments on board SRE-1 were conducted under micro-gravity conditions.

The successful launch, in-orbit operation of the on-board experiments and re-entry and recovery of SRE-1 have demonstrated India's capability in important technologies like aero-thermo structures, deceleration and flotation systems, navigation, guidance and control.

Surveillance

We have discussed the benefits of remote sensing devices earlier. Remote sensing military applications come under the rubric of surveillance. With the aid of remote sensing satellites, aircraft, tanks, bunkers etc. in enemy territory across the world can be differentiated through image processing techniques. Infrared wavelengths are also used to identify objects at night. Near-infrared images can even identify the spots from which aircraft have taken off, by sensing the heat emitted by the aircraft before leaving the place in which it was standing. Such information is of tactical importance.

Surveillance equipment requires extremely high resolution capabilities. The more a camera and image processor is able to differentiate smaller objects, the higher it is in resolution. In addition to high resolution, military surveillance also requires fast and repetitive coverage. You may think that a geostationary satellite may be well suited for this purpose, since it provides twenty-four-hour coverage. But remember, a geostationary satellite will have to be at the height of 36,000 km from the Earth. A camera that is so far away from its subject is sure to have lower resolution. High frequency repetivity and high resolution are in fact contradictory requirements. The problem is solved by having several low-Earth satellites covering the desired areas. The orbit coverage is adjusted to have frequent sighting of the desired geographical locations. Often such data is recorded on board and accessed at a safe location for further processing.

Satellite communications are vital as well for surveillance systems. Surveillance and communications are two key functions for defence preparedness, and they go hand in hand. Knowing about and understanding the preparations and movements of the enemy and passing the information speedily to various levels of the armed forces and to decision-makers are both crucial in military strategy.

When it comes to using space to send precision guided warheads, the warheads must have high precision position location data on a real time basis. These functions are achieved by space-based and ground-based tracking systems like the Global Positioning System (GPS).

These technologies have made it possible for modern nations to carry out precision guided, remotely managed warfare. This was seen in the US and allied forces' attack during the Gulf War in 1991 and again in 2003.

Missile interception

If you look at military history, you will find that there is a continuous search to blunt the most powerful weapons of the opposition. Those who have found newer technologies and techniques have emerged victorious.

When the Europeans started using guns and cannons, they had an edge over others. In our country Tipu Sultan used innovation to his advantage when he used rockets fixed with swords. But these had some problems of stabilization and therefore the targets could not be hit accurately. The British studied and improved on these rockets by adding fins to them for stabilization, and later used them in Europe against the French.

So naturally, as missiles became reliable and powerful in reach and warhead-carrying capability, research began on technologies and systems which might blunt the first strike advantages of missiles. The first thing to do of course is to track the missile, which would emanate from another territory. This is done with the help of sophisticated radars. The USA, Europe and Russia have extensive global level missile tracking capabilities using ground-based and space-based instruments and radars. These can alert the defence forces about any incoming missile.

But it is not enough simply to track the missile. Can the missile be destroyed in its early path, before it reaches one's own territory? This was the aim of the missile defence system planned by the USA during the mid-1980s, popularly called 'Star Wars'. Elements of this ambitious programme have been tested by other countries as well. The core element of such proactive defence against a missile is to hit it with another missile. This is called missile interception.

Dr Kalam elucidated the principles of missile interception in his 2003 Technology Day Talk.

A few months back, I was in a place called Chandipur-at-Sea off the coast of Orissa, where the preparations for a major missile test were being carried out. What was this test? It was to intercept an incoming missile, presumably from an adversary, by our missile. Imagine, an incoming missile is travelling at a speed of 1,200 metres per second, very high above the ground. You cannot judge it with your eyes. There are telemetry systems continuously radiating performance information about the missile. We make use of radars, which work by bouncing off radio waves and sensing the echo to find out the position and speed of the target. These radars are very powerful, so that they can detect precisely a small object hundreds of kilometres away.

Having detected a fast-moving target, what do we do next? We must then decide, 'Is this a missile aimed at us?' To do this we must make use of extremely powerful fast computers on the ground running millions of calculations per second. Based on these calculations, if we conclude that the object is indeed a missile coming towards us, then steps must be taken to intercept the target missile. What are these steps? These steps are to find out where the missile is launched from, where is it going to impact, and then to see which of our own missiles can intercept this incoming missile. You can very well imagine the minimum time available for the required operations. Having done this, the next step is to launch our own indigenously designed missile at the correct time from the designated launch pad.

Are our jobs over? No. Having launched our own missile we must guide it towards the enemy missile. This is done by guiding our own missile through a radio link to track where the enemy missile is right now. As our missile approaches the target, the missile opens its own small radar—called a seeker— to accurately locate the target and then to home in on it, intercept and destroy.

All these steps were carried out successfully by our defence scientists during November 2006 on Wheeler Island; they had a direct interception of an incoming missile which they destroyed. This is a major achievement for our country as the test involved the development and integration of many technologies, based on the work of a large number of teams. This has been made possible because of the continuous development by DRDO of various missile systems in close collaboration with industry, other national research laboratories and academic institutions. Similarly, I would suggest that industries should consolidate the cumulative development of technologies taking place in various science and technology institutions in the country and develop products using state-of-the-art technology for ensuring availability of competitive products for both national and international markets.

A more elaborate successful demonstration of the missile defence system by DRDO scientists took place on 6 March 2009. The new system is called the Ballistic Missile Defence (BMD) system. With this test, India joined an elite club of countries (USA, Russia and Israel) which possess this capability. It is planned to have an operational BMD system in India by 2011–12. This system is expected to provide a shield against the possible launch of nuclear-tipped missiles from our neighbourhood. The BMD is a very complex system involving many difficult and high precision technologies. It required many creative minds to work together towards a common goal to overcome the intellectual challenges and bring about its realization.

Space security

Till the beginning of the twentieth century, countries were concentrating on armies and navies. Technologies, techniques, strategies and tactics revolved around the use of these two armed forces. The invention of aircraft by the Wright brothers at the beginning of the twentieth century led to initial uses of these in World War I. But by World War II rapid advances in aircraft technologies had led to large-scale use of aircraft in the war for bombing and reconnaissance purposes. In the post-War years, the air force became a major element of the defence and war capabilities of most countries. Big ships were built as aircraft carriers, thus integrating airpower into the naval forces. In every military situation today, air cover is a crucial factor. The emergence of the air force took less than four decades from the first invention of the aircraft.

Similarly, missiles and space systems took less than two decades to emerge as major components of the modern defence force. In fact except for India and Japan, space programmes in other countries—including the USA, Russia, Europe and China—started with the military objectives of developing intermediate and long-range missiles. The use of satellite communication and remote sensing had strong roots of military applications as well.*

Currently, missile and space systems are the dominant technologies availed by modern defence forces which use them extensively and have integrated them in military planning, strategy and tactics. Naturally, therefore, space systems are the first to be targeted today by the potential enemy, just as armies and naval ships were targeted in earlier years and air force stations were targeted during the second half of the twentieth century.

Satellites by the laws of nature cannot be hidden or kept over one's sovereign territory. They move freely in outer space without any care for the geographical boundaries drawn through the geopolitics of peoples and nations. They are vulnerable to attacks through electronic means—for example, by jamming the satellite's communication equipment from the ground or blinding the position location and guidance equipment onboard or the surveillance camera system through powerful lasers aimed at these from the ground. Another technique of disabling satellites is through physical attack. China recently tested an Anti-Satellite (ASAT) system. USA and Russia already have extensive capabilities for ASATs.

Strictly speaking, as per the existing international laws governing space activities, interfering with satellite or launch vehicle operations of another country is not permitted. It is the equivalent of attacking another country. But war or aggression is a phenomenon that typically takes place when one or both parties does not respect the other or when they suspect each other. In desperation,

---

*Interestingly, the Internet, which is now part of every civilian home, had its origins in US military data transfer systems.

or thinking that one may have the first-strike advantage, space assets—the collective name given to all useful items in space and their support systems in space and on the ground—may be attacked. Thus space security, that is, assuring the security of space assets, has become an important element of military thinking and vital for national security. Even civilian space assets need to be secured. But everything cannot be fixed by technology alone. Parallel to technical safeguards, many countries work out mutually acceptable legal treaties for space security as well.

For many years, Dr Kalam has shown his concern for the security of space assets, especially because humanity derives tremendous benefits from space. These benefits are availed not only by spacefaring nations like the USA, Russia, the European countries, Japan, China and India, but many others who do not make satellites or even ground stations. They enjoy many civilian benefits of space for faster communication, natural resources management, logistics management through GPS, weather monitoring etc. It will be a sad day if such beautiful gains of human knowledge which are available universally are obstructed through insecurity regarding space assets.

This is what Dr Kalam had to say on the matter as part of his multimedia teleconference address titled 'World Space Vision' to the Centre for Aerospace Strategic Studies (CESA) and the National Centre for Space Studies (CNES), France on 5 June 2007.

International Space Force (ISF)

When enormous societal and economic commitments have been made by nations with space infrastructure, the main security concern is that outer space should be free of weapons. We must recognize the necessity for the world space community to avoid terrestrial geo-political conflict to be drawn into outer space, thus threatening the space assets belonging to all mankind. Allowing space to become a battlefield could cause serious harm to society. There exist strong international norms and deep-seated public opinion around the world against space weaponization. Any unilateral action which upsets the stability of space is against the interest of the entire mankind. Multilateral approaches are required to ensure that the use of outer space is in conformity with international law and in the interest of maintaining peace and security and promoting international cooperation. Hence, I suggest the creation of an International Space Force (ISF) made up of all nations wishing to participate and contribute to the protection of world space assets in a manner that will enable the peaceful exploitation of space on a global cooperative basis. The ISF will safeguard the global space assets, protect against the militarization of space, engage in space rescues, space debris management and monitoring and defence against asteroids.

As both of us (Kalam and Rajan) had our initial careers in space research, this book has started with the first few chapters on different aspects of space. There is, of course, much more to say on space applications, satellite design, astronomy, planetary sciences, space biology etc. But we need to remind the reader that though space is always exciting, there are also other areas of science and technology and their applications which are equally intriguing. They may not be flashed in the media too often, but the intellectual challenges they pose are equally attractive. Their uses and benefits cover many vital aspects of human life.

We will shift to some of these other areas of science in the next two sections of this book.

THE EARTH

Chapter 4

THE EARTH, OUR HOME

Most of us do not even look at the ground beneath our feet; we feel it is unimportant, and dirty. In cities we cover the soil with asphalt and concrete, so that we aren't even aware of its existence. But though we may not think about it too often, the earth is the source of life on our planet; without it we would not exist.

Our Earth appears to be unique, not only in our galaxy but perhaps in the entire universe, including all other galaxies. Even if it were not the only one of its kind, another Earth similar to ours would be very very rare.

Within the solar system, the Earth is in an optimally advantageous position to nurture life. A planet that is too near the Sun (such as Mercury and Venus) is too hot and full of hot gases; therefore it cannot sustain life. One that is too far away from the Sun (such as Jupiter, Saturn and even Mars) is too cold, as the Sun's rays are not strong enough here; it is not possible for living forms to survive in such a climate.

Why does distance from the Sun matter so much?

The intensity of light rays is inversely proportional to the square of the distance they have to travel. In mathematical terms this can be expressed as $1/R^2$, where R is the distance. In simple terms the intensity of light rays at a distance of one kilometre from the source

---

is 1/1 km^2, but at a distance of 10 km it becomes 1/10 km^2, which is not ten times less but a hundred times less. This is the reason that we do not feel the intensity of starlight on Earth, though many stars are many thousands of times more powerful than the Sun—they are simply too far away.

Why 1/R^2?

Very simple. The light of the Sun spreads uniformly in all directions. If something is uniformly spread in all directions you can imagine that at any distance from the source it is like being on the surface of a sphere. On an expanding sphere, as we move away from the centre, the surface area of a sphere can be measured as $4\pi R^2$, where R is the radius. As we move away from the Sun, the entire intensity of the Sun is uniformly spread over a larger sphere, over a larger $4\pi R^2$. The more the value of R is, the more thinly spread the energy is. Hence the intensity of the Sun's rays can be measured as 1/R^2.

It is because of the same principle that if we want to use more light from a light bulb we do not allow it to spread in all directions, focusing it instead in the one direction we want, with a reflector at the back; spotlights use this method, so does a car headlight. But the Sun does not have a reflector to focus its rays (if it did, for some part of the year, as the Earth orbits around the Sun, we would have been in the dark!).

The Earth's position in the solar system appears to be perfect in order to sustain life. As a matter of fact, detailed calculations will show that it is not exactly so; in terms of distance from the Sun, the Earth should have been somewhat colder, and the origin of life would have been difficult. So where does the extra heat come from? It comes from the atmosphere that surrounds the Earth.

The atmosphere is not so thick as to cut the Sun's rays out completely. It allows solar rays—almost the full optical spectrum of VIBGYOR and other rays in that range—to penetrate it and reach the surface of the Earth where we live. But it cuts out, through the ozone layer, ultraviolet rays which are dangerous to life forms. When the Sun's rays fall on the Earth some of these are reflected or scattered and go back into the atmosphere, directed towards outer space. But not all of these are let out. They interact with various molecules in the atmosphere. The molecules are heated up as a result, and the end effect is to heat up the atmosphere. In addition, as the Sun's rays interact with the soil, living beings and the atmosphere, heat is generated. Plants and some organisms in water use the Sun's rays to produce energy for themselves, heating the water in the process. Water helps retain a lot of solar heat, thus contributing to the warmth of the Earth, to a level conducive to life. Dead animals and vegetative wastes generate methane which can burn, producing more heat. Remember the Earth is a great factory of life, chemicals, fire, geothermal eruptions etc. All the heat generated in this factory goes up from the surface towards outer space. But the heat is not allowed to escape easily. Many molecules in the atmosphere (carbon dioxide molecules for example) trap the heat and keep it circulating between the earth, air and water. This effect—called the 'greenhouse effect'—is very useful in keeping the Earth warm.

Let us look briefly at exactly how the greenhouse effect works.

In the colder parts of India or in the hilly regions, you will find that when it is very cold outside, many plants tend to shrink and wilt, and new germinations from seeds do not take place. Even curd does not form from milk. All these processes require warmth. To make curd in winter the milk is kept warm before it curdles— the vessel is covered with a shawl or thick blanket and kept in a closed space where air does not circulate. There is a small greenhouse effect that takes place between the covering shawl and the vessel, and the curd forms as a result of the warmth.

Similarly, to protect plants or flowers from the harshness of the cold outside or to help seeds germinate, plastic tents are used to cover the plants. Cold air from the outside cannot flow into these tents easily. Inside the plastic, the Sun's rays creates a greenhouse.

The heat generated inside the tent does not go outside as the plastic is not transparent to infrared rays the way it is to rays in the VIBGYOR region.

An extreme example of the greenhouse effect, one that can make life very uncomfortable, is what happens inside your car if you park in the sun when there is no shade available. The inside of the car gets so hot that you will sweat when you go in. We sometimes keep a small gap in the window to allow convection. But then there are car thieves to worry about!

The greenhouse effect in the atmosphere has given us a lot of benefits. In fact, it has made life possible. It sustains the whole biosphere as well as the hydrosphere. In fact, the Earth–atmosphere–ocean combination is crucial for us to benefit from the Sun's rays, and to live.

But the dynamic balance of the greenhouse effect is also delicate. If we generate too much heat in the Earth through our activities and also overgenerate 'greenhouse effect producing molecules' (such as carbon dioxide, methane, nitrogen oxide etc.) and let them into the atmospheric envelope, the greenhouse will start going from gentle warmth to excessive heat. Even the rise of the Earth's temperature by a few degrees may melt the ice on the polar caps. The delicate balance of life forms in the sea would be affected as a result. Coastal zones would be submerged due to the excessive flow of water released from the ice. Those are some of the current worries about 'climate change' due to human-originated (anthropogenic) changes to the Earth and its envelope. To reduce such human-induced changes, it is necessary to reduce energy consumption to the utmost minimum, reduce wastes (through the use of recycled material), and also target on reduction of some of the greenhouse molecules in the atmosphere.

The origins of the Earth

There was a time when some of our ancestors believed the Earth was the centre of the universe. We now know that not even our galaxy has that role. The universe is huge, and we have barely begun to understand it. As more scientific researches have been undertaken with increasingly advanced observational technologies, we have come to know a great deal more about the solar system. But there is still much that is unknown.

Currently accepted theories infer that the solar system began as a spinning cloud of gas and dust of matter. It is estimated that the initial mass of this spinning cloud was about 10 to 20 per cent more than the combined mass of the solar system now.

Current theories also estimate the Sun cloud to have formed about 5 billion years ago. Over a period of about 400 million years, the cloud contracted under its own force of gravity, the heavy centre attracting the dust of matter inwards from the outer region. The atoms came closer to each other and solar density increased through this process of contraction. The middle bulge of the Sun started appearing as a result, and, over time, the materials around the outer disc of the Sun turned into more solid dust-like particles. These in turn accumulated more matter; thus the planets were formed and spun off.

The Earth would have been spun off from the Sun about 4.5 billion years ago. It was not at all like what we see today. The spun-off matter, still very hot, would have undergone several drastic internal adjustments in its structure (the remnants of which continue even today in the form of earthquakes and tremors).

Also, the Earth's geography, which defines current-day nationhood, politics, even culture, was not what it is today. The continents—the Americas, Europe, Africa, Asia, Australia—were not separated from each other. The land masses on Earth floated around for hundreds of millions of years, as the Earth was very hot and in a molten stage. The forces of gravity of the huge mass and the centrifugal forces arising from the spinning and orbital motions acted and adjusted against each other. These violent adjustments and readjustments in the interior parts of the Earth gave rise to many of the valuable natural resources we use today (coal, oil, natural gas and various minerals).

The first life forms, unicellular bacteria-like organisms, appeared on Earth some 3.5 billion years ago, after about 1 billion years of internal turmoil. Blue algae were the first organisms that started the process of photosynthesis, i.e. the use of the Sun's rays to produce chemicals conducive to life and provide nutrition. This brought oxygen to the Earth's atmosphere, and thus the proliferation of life became possible. Then came more complex organisms, which evolved over many millions of years. The appearance of the first human being (*Homo sapiens*) is not even a million years old—it was around 200,000 years ago.*

Water

We all know that water is vital to life. If you look at the Earth on a globe or in a flat map, you will see blue, denoting water, all over—in the massive oceans and seas, and even in the lakes and rivers that are a part of the land mass. Still we are worried nowadays about water shortage. Some even like to predict 'water wars'. Why is this?

According to estimates from UN agencies, the total amount of water on Earth is about 1,400 million km^3. What is a cubic kilometre (km^3)? Imagine a big cube that is 1 km long, 1 km wide and 1 km deep. Now imagine it completely filled with water. The water contained there can be measured as one cubic kilometre.

---

*More information on the Earth can be found in a series of inexpensive books brought out by Vigyan Prasar of the Department of Science and Technology, Government of India, and on the website http://www.vigyanprasan.gov.in. We have also drawn on Biman Basu's book *Planet Earth in a Nutshell* for some of the information in this and later chapters.

Let us try to understand just how much water this is. You know how much a litre of water is—it is what a bottle of mineral water contains. If we imagine a cube 1 metre long, 1 metre wide and 1 metre deep, it would contain one cubic metre ($1 m^3$) of water.

1 cubic metre ($1 m^3$)	=	1000 litre (one kilolitre)
1 cubic kilometre ($1 km^3$)	=	1 billion cubic metres
	=	1000 billion litres
	=	1 trillion litres

On average pure water 1 litre in volume weighs about 1 kilogram. $1 km^3$ of water is about 1 trillion litres and if we are comfortable with tonnes (1000 kg = 1 tonne) then $1 km^3$ water weighs about 1 billion tonnes.

The Earth contains about 1,400 million km^3 of water. You can do your own calculations about how many litres or how heavy that is. But make sure you have a calculator that goes up to many digits!

Of this huge amount of water on Earth, about 98 per cent is made up of oceans and seas, which contain 75 per cent of the total water on Earth. Fresh water forms only a small part, about 2.7 per cent of the total quantity. Of this tiny portion of 2.7 per cent about 75.2 per cent is frozen as glaciers and ice in the polar regions, and a further 22.6 per cent is present as ground water, most of which lies too far underground to be used. Thus about 97.8 per cent of the tiny 2.7 per cent of fresh water available on Earth is not easily accessible to human beings. Only a small part, 2.2 per cent, that is, about 0.06 per cent of the total water available on Earth is accessible for human use. This is why water is so precious.

This tiny fraction of fresh water is renewed and refreshed every year by the factory of the Sun as part of the natural water cycle. Water evaporates into the atmosphere and comes back to Earth in the form of snow and rain, and also melts down from the snow in glaciers. This refreshed and renewed water is available in lakes and rivers, in atmospheric moisture, in the soil and vegetation. All living beings depend on water for survival; a significant part of our bodies are made of water, though only a comparatively small portion is directly consumed by us. This is why it is so important to keep the extremely limited fresh water resources on Earth very carefully protected from pollution, to sustain all life forms.

It is also important to understand the close interconnections between the soil, the oceans and the atmosphere. If we pollute the atmosphere with harmful chemicals, they will come back to the ground through rain. You must have heard of the phenomenon of 'acid rain' in some developed countries some decades ago, due to acidic gases emitted by automobile and factories. Similarly, if we dump our waste into the oceans, not only will it pollute the water and kill marine life, but it will come back to our coasts like oil spills.

We can only cover a small part of the many exciting aspects of the Earth and oceans here. Those of you who are young now can have an exciting career researching the many yet-unknown aspects of life on Earth. One of the most interesting things about the research being done now is the use of space platforms to observe and understand the Earth. We have learnt a lot more about the Earth since 1957, the start of the Space Era.

Cartography

Those who explored the Earth and the oceans in earlier centuries used several instruments to give them a sense of direction. One constant companion which helped them in finding direction was the magnetic compass. But even when they did not have instruments, they turned to nature. The Sun during the daytime and the Moon and stars during the night were a great help. Most people in earlier generations residing in villages were familiar with the positions of stars, and of bright planets like Venus, Mars and Jupiter which are visible to the naked eye. From the positions of the stars and visible planets, they could determine the time of day, the day of the month and the progress of the year. This is a skill that is sadly lost to most people today.

As far as measurements are concerned, too, the early adventurers and travellers used parts of their own bodies—the length of a footstep (about a foot), an elbow length (about half a yard), a finger length (about three inches)—as units. Even now, in Tamil Nadu, the jasmine garlands which women wear are measured by the elbow length of the person who sells them.

Over a period of time, the early explorers created maps to describe details of places they had visited, and to help future adventurers in their travels. Water bodies, mountains, forests and deserts were marked, and the boundaries between countries were also shown. Within countries, rulers started using mapping techniques to earmark agricultural fields and other land areas; this helped in the proper estimation and recovery of taxes. While such elements of land records and agricultural taxes are referred to in the *Arthashastra* by Kautilya, the formal land record systems as they exist in India now were initiated by Todar Mal during Emperor Akbar's regime.

The discipline of making maps, delineating various forms of land use, whether it is at the level of a village or a street or on a global scale, is called cartography.

If you look at your mobile phone while travelling, you will see that it tells you that you are at the Gateway of India or at India Gate, in a particular mall or office, at the airport or a railway station. This useful information is a product of cartography coupled with other disciplines like computers, software, communications etc. The position at which you are on Earth need not be calculated any longer through the positions of the Sun, Moon, planets, stars or through the aid of a magnetic compass, or measured or charted by individuals. The use of navigation satellites coupled with a network of ground receivers does the job, providing information on GPS (Global Positioning System). GPS systems can determine exactly where you are when you are talking on your mobile. Through applications such as Google Earth, they can also show you a detailed map of any place on Earth.

Dr Kalam has spoken often on the subject of Earth resources. When he participated in the 26th Congress of the Indian Cartographic Association (INCA) in New Delhi on 22 November 2006, the topic of his inaugural address was 'Cartographers: Partners in National Development'. Here is an excerpt from that speech.

India has a vision of transforming itself into a developed nation before 2020. There are a number of missions which need inputs from cartography technologies that will certainly accelerate the process of development. Programmes such as the Bharat Nirman Programme including PURA (Providing Urban Amenities in Rural Areas), networking of rivers, infrastructure development in sixty-three cities through the Jawaharlal Nehru National Urban Renewable Mission (JNNURM), mapping of earthquake-prone areas and recurring floods in north Bihar and Assam require vital inputs at the stage of planning and implementation. The mission of INCA should be to assist the implementation of the developed India vision using their core competence in cartography in partnership with ISRO, NRSA, Survey of India, State Remote Sensing centres, thematic map-making organizations, Indian Remote Sensing industries, academia, research institutions and other IT organizations.

As a part of physical connectivity, link roads emanating from PURA clusters joining the main roads have to be planned in such a way that they can meet the growing traffic resulting out of higher economic activity in the PURA clusters. A combination of ground survey, satellite remote sensing data and aerial pictures has to be used to derive relevant maps at large scales better than 1:10,000 and even at the level of 1:20,000 as appropriate, in a timebound manner within the next two years.

JNNURM envisages provision of modern drainage systems, provision of drinking water in each house, electrical and electronic connectivity, rainwater harvesting and water recycling, and provision of congestion-free roads. JNNURM is a timebound programme. It is very important for cartographers to provide cartographic data for each of the sixty-three cities and towns, using the satellite imagery coupled with GIS (Geographic Information System). They should first establish the existing road network with contours, green areas, location of original water bodies, existing sewage and drainage systems. New alignment has to be provided keeping a fifty years' growth profile in mind and updated at an interval of ten years. Availing temporal information obtained through satellite remote sensing will enable better planning and regular monitoring. Based on this study, they must provide new connectivity contours, the new sewage system alignment, possible transportation of sewage system remains after treatment and above all a multi-layered road system to remove traffic congestion. It should be made mandatory for the city administration to use such data and information for decision making.

Dr Kalam then moves on to the issues of disaster management, for which mapping is crucial, since, with accurate mapping, one can concentrate on providing preventive measures in disaster-prone areas.

Disaster management

Earthquakes: Though India is rich in natural resources, many parts of India also face different types of disasters such as earthquakes, incessant downpours leading to localized floods, droughts, avalanches and landslides in hilly areas, storms and tsunamis. It may not be possible to avert the natural disasters, but the suffering and misery due to the loss of life and the adverse socio-economic impact can be minimized. First the mapping of earthquake-prone areas with suitable details enables the detailed precautions in construction and emergency actions. A powerful enough earthquake just a few seconds in duration can make current maps suddenly out of date, at the same time severing power lines, gas mains and water pipes. Secondary disasters such as landslides may have taken place in some areas. Satellite images can provide updated views of how the landscape has been affected, while images before and after the event enable authoritative damage assessment as a basis for planning remedial action.

Flood and water management: I have observed certain unique features in the river system of Bihar. Though the Ganga, the main river, flows from the west to the east, there are two types of river flows coming into the Ganga. Because of the flow from both directions no water is saved and everything goes into the sea. Also, the main floodbearing river, the Kosi, when it comes into Bihar is already in the plains. So we have to find innovative flood management techniques. Cartographers should provide high-resolution maps in partnership with agencies involved in satellite imagery and aerial photography for planning water harvesting and water management systems leading to flood control even in the steep slopes of the hill area.

Flood control through layered wells: There is an urgent need to find long-term solutions to control floods, and store and utilize the surplus water during droughts. In the Gangetic region, I have recommended the construction of layered wells at the entry points of the Kosi river. Normally the floodwater has certain dynamic flow conditions. The layered wells will assist gradual reduction in dynamic flow velocity after filling each storage well. The water thus stored will be useful during shortage periods. Similar solutions can be found for the northeastern region. The complex problem today is to find the location of multi-layered wells at the entry point of floods arising from the Himalayan region. Innovation lies in finding a suitable place in finding a solution even though the Indian-side entry-point contours are very steep. Hence, there is a big challenge to cartographers to provide location of multi-layered wells, taking into account the part of the flood water movement.

Dr Kalam goes on to talk about satellite technology enabled cartography, which involves the use of stereo images. One thing that gives a special capability to human beings over other animals and birds is the fact that human beings can see in three dimensions with a large amount of detail. This is due to the fact that human beings have their two eyes set very close to each other.

A cow, a lion or a bird has its two eyes located far away from each other. Animals and birds need to have good coverage of their sides and know what is going on behind their backs to locate their prey or to detect predators. Such a wide coverage is obtained by a large separation of the eyes. We cannot see what is behind us. At best we can see a movement away from our shoulders, if we are alert. Animals and birds have a good back vision, but they lose the details of a three-dimensional coverage. They have an image closer to the two-dimensional portrait a photograph provides, but not the clear three-dimensional depth view that we have.

The reason we have this three-dimensional view is because of stereo imaging—our eyes which are very close to each other provide overlapping images to the brain, which is then able to construct a three-dimensional picture. Similarly, if two cameras are kept very close to each other and take overlapping images, then we can create a three-dimensional picture with the right elevation. The stereo picture will show all the details of heights, depths and contours. Even small ripples and whirls in water can be identified. Such images would be immensely useful for both civilian and military purposes.

On a 3-D image of the terrain, we can see even the smallest differences in heights. These are called contours. If these are stored in digitized form, the map is called a digital terrain map, and the information available therein is called a digital elevation model.

Let us now look at the rest of Dr Kalam's speech.

Technology-enabled cartography

To address all the inputs needed for the above programmes, we need to use the latest scientific technologies and tools. In this context, the application of Information Technology in the form of GIS, satellite remote sensing, satellite photo-grammatry, satellite communication and the Internet play a vital role. India has planned for a series of satellites specifically for cartographic applications. The first in the series, CARTOSAT-I, launched in May 2005, is the first high-resolution satellite that collects the details of terrain surfaces in stereo mode with the spatial resolution of 2.5 metres. As of today, I understand that more than 90 per cent of the country is covered with stereo images. These images could also be used for better urban planning, and cadastral level information of land and water resources. This satellite mission has enabled developing a Digital Elevation Model (DEM). This elevation model is useful in GIS environment, providing a terrain model to facilitate drainage network analysis, watershed demarcation, erosion mapping, contour generation and quantitative analyses like location–distance–area–volume calculation. The DEM could also provide scene simulation and fly-through visualization of the terrain. I am happy to note that the Department of Space has launched a mission called CARTODEM for generating a DEM of the entire country using an indigenously developed software package. The elevation accuracy of the DEM will be better than 8 metres. It is expected that by the middle of 2007, a major part of our country will be covered by the DEM. Such an input should be made use of effectively by the cartographers of the country for generating quality input data for PURA planning, design and development of state-level waterways, urban planning and disaster management. As you may be aware, CARTOSAT-II, capable of collecting the terrain features with better than one metre spatial resolution, is to be launched in January 2007. I am sure that the country will have satellites for acquiring details at sub-metre level in the next five years.

Advances in computer sciences and space technologies today provide us the capability not only to integrate diverse data sets but also with real time communication of data from far-flung areas. Referencing of these data sets to their geographical locations has given rise to a powerful Geographical Information System (GIS) which is finding increasing use in almost every facet of our day-to-day lives, be it as an administrator or a planner or as an executive monitoring a project or a tourist finding his way through navigation systems. These applications demand dynamic integration and visualization which in turn provide challenges to the cartographer as to how to integrate and process the data in real time and provide the visualization of output as per user requirements. Yet another challenge to be addressed by the cartographic community is how to ensure data integrity, interoperability and accuracy while fusing data from disparate data sources. Advances in other technologies like GPS, mobile telephones, digital cartography and photogrammatry will also complement the cartographers in their endeavours for national development.

Cartography has come a long way from the days of Ptolemy and is playing a major role in our lives through new technologies such as GIS and GPS. I am told that most of the mapping of the Western world today is done in Delhi, Hyderabad and Bangalore. There is a need for a campaign to increase the awareness of the common man regarding the utility of geo-spatial data and its use. The cartographic community has a key role to play in national development and I am sure you will provide value-added services to all national missions.

Chapter 5

THE EARTH AND ITS RESOURCES

In the previous chapter we briefly discussed how the Earth was formed about 4.5 billion years ago and how the turbulent activities inside the Earth led to the formation of our natural resources, from ground water to coal to uranium. We have discussed India's material resources in detail in the chapter titled 'Materials and the Future' in our book *India 2020: A Vision for the New Millennium* where we have also touched on India's comparative advantages with respect to certain materials; we will not repeat that information here. ·

How are these materials formed? The elements, from hydrogen to uranium, are made up of molecules—from the simple atom of hydrogen (which is very light) to the complex uranium. The high temperatures and more importantly the high pressures generated by the shrinking molten material inside the Earth in its formative years crushed the atoms of the elements and forced molecules to come closer and closer. The more the pressure, the more the density of atoms and molecules, leading to the formation of the higher elements. Crushed vegetation (trees etc.) created big blocks of carbon which we now see as coal. With even more pressure, the same material would become diamonds. Different layers of the earth also contributed to the formation of different natural resources; we shall look at these later in this chapter.

Mining

Mining is the process of retrieving mineral resources from the earth for human use. At the inaugural address at the nineteenth World Mining Congress and Expo 2003 in New Delhi on 1 November 2003, Dr Kalam described his vision for the Indian mining industry.

Mining has provided the answer to the manufacturing and energy needs of humanity in the past century. Coal has been a major contributor in providing energy security during this period. It is possible that this pattern may change and there could be emphasis on uranium- and thorium-based power plants during the later part of the twenty-first century in addition to an emphasis on renewable energy sources.

Coal

As far as India is concerned, 80 per cent of our mining is in coal and the balance 20 per cent is in various metals and other raw materials such as gold, copper, iron, lead, bauxite, zinc and uranium. In spite of the economic liberalization of 1991 the mining sector has not attracted major investments. This is possibly due to problems in land acquisition, development of infrastructure, transportation systems, social engineering and community development involved in major greenfield site projects. There is a need to re-look at the total management solution for attracting investment in new mines. The solution has to lead to the creation of joint venture institutions with the Central government, state governments and the private sector as partners. The facilitation for the project through provision of land, infrastructural development, community development etc. can be done by government agencies whereas the investment in the mine and the associated technological inputs can come from the private sector. In addition, the private sector must have the freedom to run the mine in a cost-effective manner.

This may be a long-term solution for our future mines in the country and it will have unique opportunities for both the government and the private sector to work together for national development.

India is a global player in coal mining and is the third largest producer of coal though the productivity in underground mining requires a quantum jump from 0.5 ton per man-year to 3 tons per man-year in the immediate near term. In addition, we have to work on clean coal technology to prevent the effects of global warming and environmental pollution. For a long time we have been talking about integrated gasification and combined cycle technology. NTPC, BHEL and CSIR laboratories should work on this project in a mission mode. Coal India and other producers should help in this project by contributing in beneficiation and washing of the coal input. We should have a timebound programme for getting the results from this project. I am sure that these results will have far-reaching implications on the choice of technology for all our future mining applications.

There have been major developments in mining technology over the last few decades. The condition of coal miners today is not as bad as it was at the time of Karl Marx, which led him to write forcefully about their fate. There are many technologies in place now that can ensure safety in the mines and greatly reduce pollution levels, which have to do with the dust in the mines as well as the destruction of the soil on the top surface. But while developed countries have made a lot of progress towards providing safe and pollution-free mines, developing countries like India have a long way to go in this regard. To quote Dr Kalam:

All mining operations today involve continuous use of explosives, thereby generating high noise levels, vibrations and shocks, and very high levels of dust pollution. They also take away very large areas as explosive safety zones and environment safety zones. Can our researchers evolve a technology for using high power laser systems for safe, pollution-free, precision mining?

―――――――――――――――――

Continuing with his observations on some of the issues crucial to mining in India, Dr Kalam says:

―――――――――――――――――

Challenges in Jharia

Jharia coalfield in Jharkhand is the richest coal-bearing area in the country which contains large quantities of high-grade coking coal. However, this area also has a large number of mine fires which have been burning for several decades. I am reminded of an incident when I was travelling from Sindri to Dhanbad. Hundreds of villagers rushed to my car and narrated the heating and spot-fire which regularly takes place near their houses. A major challenge to the mining community is that of tackling fires which have engulfed large and densely populated coal-bearing areas. Similar problems would have been experienced in many parts of the world. This Congress can take a lead in finding a technological, cost-effective, safe and minimum disturbance solution to this problem by focusing the attention of the best minds in the field.

Mines safety

I am happy to know that our mines safety performance has been continuously improving in the past few years. This is indicated by the drop in fatal accidents, serious accidents, injuries and the death rate per million tonnes. However, we have a long way to reach zero-accident situations. To enable this, we have to apply legislative, promotional and operational measures on a continuous basis. Some of the operational measures to improve safety performance include a participative approach of tackling the problem in which all the stakeholders participate in the design of an integrated risk management system. The integrated approach would cover risk evaluation, identifying hazards, analysing, prioritizing, ranking and monitoring risks. It requires a thorough understanding of the finer aspects of disaster management and recovery.

I suggest that the Congress creates a website: 'Web of Life— Mines Safety'. This could be a forum through which many countries can exchange their views on aspects of mine accidents. We could gather the data for the past twenty-five years and use the very best of data mining tools to take us to a world of accident-free mining. The next World Mining Congress must have a special session and theme devoted to the international experiences in mines safety and their possible localization. The deliberations and recommendations thereon will lead to the evolution of feasible designs and design standards for accident-free mining.

The layers of the Earth and oceans

Before we continue with our discussion of minerals and mining, it would be interesting to look at how the Earth and oceans are layered. Suppose you had the power to dig through the 6,000 km of the Earth's surface to arrive at the centre of the Earth, what would it be like? Would it be similar to gazing down a deep well or the dug-up foundation for a very tall multistoreyed building? The fact is, no one has ever seen what it is like at the centre of the Earth, so we can only guess. The maximum distance anyone has drilled a hole into the earth is about 12.5 km, in Russia. The rest of the details we have gathered about the surface of the Earth are derived from observations through complex instruments and scientific and mathematical models developed by geoscientists. Geoscientists—that is, scientists who study the earth and oceans— have used thousands of records of how earthquakes propagate from their centre of disturbance (the epicentre) to other parts of the Earth, to derive the densities of the different parts of the Earth's interior. Geoscientists use earthquake waves to study the interior of the Earth in the same way that cardiologists use ultrasound waves to study the inside of the heart.

Scientists have divided the surface of the Earth into four broad regions, progressing downwards from the top:

- The crust
- The mantle
- The liquid inner core
- The solid inner core.

The crust: The crust under the land mass extends to about 35 km on an average. In the case of the crust below the ocean floor—known as oceanic crust—it is limited to about 10 km below the bottom of the ocean. Just below the crust there is a 40,000 km long network of active volcanoes and fissures. These activities create new igneous rocks, also called basalts, and as a result about 17 km³ of new crust is formed every year. Hawaii and Iceland were formed quite recently by such basalts: Iceland is only about 20,000 years old. As a result, these areas have high geothermal activities which are used effectively to generate clean energy.

We find it difficult to dig even 1 metre below the Earth's surface. With machines we can dig a few metres, and boring drills such as the rigs used by companies searching for oil and natural gas can dig up to a few kilometres. But most of the mining that we do takes place within 1 km of the surface.

Though 35 km of crust can look big to us, compared to the size of the Earth, the crust is like the thin skin of a large fruit.

The crust just below the land mass—known as continental crust—is made up of crystalline rocks, dominated by quartz (silicon dioxide) and silicates. At the top of the crust the temperature, naturally, is like that of air; as we go down the crust temperature rises sharply, going up to about 870°C where the crust interfaces with the mantle. In a way the top of the crust—which is about 10 km thick—protects us from the wrath of the inner heat, just as the lower levels of the atmosphere—about 15 km thick—protects us from the terrible cold of outer space.

The Earth's crust is made of two rock types: granite (the hard and crystalline rocks you see as a polished flooring surface) and basalt, a more dense solidified lava. Granite is usually found in the continental crust while basalt occurs in the oceanic crust. Remember that the oceanic crust continues below the continental crust as well. In actuality the continental crust, which is much lighter, floats on top of the basaltic oceanic crust.

The crust is not one single homogeneous unit. It is made up of many pieces called plates. These plates 'float' on the soft, elastic mantle between the crust and the mantle. The plates normally have a smooth fluid movement, but sometimes, with the build-up of pressure, they can stick to each other or collide with each other. This is what causes earthquakes.

The mantle: This layer, just under the crust, extends to almost half the radius of the Earth, about 2,900 km. The mantle is made up of solid rock but due to the extreme heat in the area it behaves like a viscous liquid. It is made up mostly of molten silicate rocks rich in iron and magnesium; most of the heat of the Earth comes from it. The mantle contributes to almost two-thirds of the Earth's mass.

There are cooler and warmer parts in the mantle. Therefore there is a powerful upward convection in the molten mass (similar to the way in which winds are generated when warmer air is pushed upwards by the colder air). These currents make the continental plates of the crust move. This is the reason for the 'continental drift' which causes continents to move about on Earth; millions of years ago, this movement separated Australia from the Asian land mass, and, when India (Gondwanaland) collided with the Asian land mass, the Himalayas were created.

Most gemstones like diamonds and garnets are formed inside the mantle. High pressure depths of greater than 150 km create the compact crystal structure of a diamond. Rapidly rising convective currents of molten rocks then carry the diamonds up to the surface, which is where they are mined.

The metallic core: One-third of the Earth's mass is in its core. Most of the core is made up of liquid iron alloyed with nickel. However, the central part (at a depth of about 5,150 km and about 850 km in radius) is solid. The temperature of the outer part of the core is around 4000^0C to 5000^0C. The absolute centre of the Earth is at around 5500^0C to 7500^0C—hotter than the surface of the Sun! It is interesting to think about this—that the heart of the planet we live on is hotter than the Sun itself.

One important character given to the Earth by this inner core is its magnetism. The iron core behaves like a dynamo, therefore currents are produced, and hence magnetism. The Earth, as you know, is a huge magnet. This is why we can find our direction on Earth with the help of a magnetic compass. The Earth's magnetic force lines spread out into outer space, and regulates many high energy particles in space from directly hitting us.

Minerals

Coming back to mining, many bounties of nature like rocks, marble and granite are garnered by quarrying, while other minerals like coal, gas, petroleum crude, various metallic ores, gold, diamonds etc. are obtained by mining or drilling deep into the earth. Most of these treasures are found within the crust. Imagine how much we are getting merely by 'scratching' the surface!

Early human findings were iron ores, copper etc. which occur very near the Earth's surface, sometimes on it. We used iron and copper to make agricultural and household implements, and weapons as well. It took us more time to discover coal, petroleum etc.—and these discoveries led eventually to the industrial revolution. After mastering these energy sources, human beings could dig deeper to get higher-quality iron and also other useful metals like aluminium and titanium. Plastics were also developed from petroleum. Later, because of multidisciplinary technological strengths—advanced mechanical and metallurgical knowledge combined with chemical engineering skills—much higher elements (i.e. those that have hundreds of protons and neutrons crowded together in a nucleus) were discovered. Some elements are even heavier than uranium and more difficult to form; they are therefore not abundant in nature.

India is not blessed with much uranium. Of the little we have, administrative and political difficulties have put several constraints on its mining. We do have thorium in plenty, but deriving nuclear (electric) power form thorium is not an easy process. Researchers worldwide are working on easier ways of making electricity from thorium; India is also active in thorium research. But meanwhile, the uranium that we need has to be supplied by other countries. Since uranium can also be used to make a nuclear bomb, its supply is strictly controlled.

When we talk of mining, we must remember that almost all the mining we do takes place on land. Some drilling for oil and petroleum takes place just off the coast (e.g. at Bombay High). However, the land mass on Earth is comparatively small—it comprises only around 25 per cent of the Earth's surface. What about the minerals that lie in the crust under the oceans and seas? It is very difficult to reach these, since one has to contend with the immense volume and weight of water that comes in the way. There have been many attempts to mine the materials that lie under the sea. India has also undertaken several experiments in this area (details are available on the website of the Department of Oceans—now called the Earth Commission). Future human engineering capabilities, say four to five decades from now, may allow us to recover precious minerals from the sea bed. For the youth of today and the coming generations, this may be one of the greatest challenges, just as the conquest of space was in the 1950s and 1960s.

Dr Kalam has spoken often about India's mineral and material resources. In his inaugural address at the fourteenth annual conference of the Indian Nuclear Society at Kalpakkam on 17 December 2003, he discussed our nuclear energy resources.

———————————————

Our modest uranium resources can support the generation of about 15,000 MW through the present generation of Pressurized Heavy Water Reactors (PHWR) which consume less than one per cent of our uranium resource. The recycling of PU-239 along with the balance uranium in depleted form to a second stage Fast Breeder Reactor (FBR) will provide us access to about 130 times more energy potential from our limited uranium reserve. Finally we have to fall back on waste thorium resource (which is about one-third of the world's total thorium resource) for our energy security. For this we have to introduce thorium in the blanket zone of second stage FBRs at an appropriate growth level of installed nuclear capacity. This would enable us to build an inventory of U-233 (from thorium) for use in the third stage of our nuclear power programme based on yet another type of fast breeder reactor using thorium U-233 MOX fuel in the core.

India possesses pilot scale experience in thorium U-233 fuel cycling including experience in building the research reactor Kamini. However we need to master all the technologies at the front end and the back end of the thorium U-233 fuel cycle at a plant scale to address all the technological problems involved in thorium utilization. We should plan to build the first thorium fuel-based advance heavy water reactor with a capacity of 1000 MW immediately.

———————————————

Elsewhere, Dr Kalam talks about garnering minerals not from the Earth's surface or ocean beds but from a different source altogether—other planets and the Moon. In fact, space might well be easier to mine than the depths of the ocean.

―――――――――

Minerals from other planets

Human life has been continuing for millions of years. It had been a long journey for mankind from the Stone Age to the Bronze Age, the Iron Age and so on. We have now reached a stage when material is available abundantly from Mother Earth. But it is not a renewable resource, one day it will exhaust itself. The demand for minerals is expected to grow very fast due to increasing levels of consumption, infrastructure development and growth of the economy. The emergence of a vibrant middle class has created demand for base metal products in addition to the traditional demand for gold and silver. Hence we have to expand our knowledge to add value to the materials presently available and preserve them for future use. Within the next few decades, we will encounter a totally new situation of acute shortages of water, energy and minerals. No single nation will be able to handle the situation by itself. Humanity will require mega missions to harness solar energy, drinking water from sea water through desalination process, and minerals from other planets. This will involve innovation and research in satellite based remote sensing of other planets, robotics, mining equipment, mining operations, extraction, beneficiation, processing and transportation.

―――――――――

Those of you who are daring, who dare to imagine, can think of many more possibilities for mining in the future. But remember, we need to study the ecological impact of mining before continuing to extract natural resources from the Earth. Future researches in natural resources are going to depend primarily on knowledge derived from science. Mining from nature will be possible only when you first mine your mind. Remember what Albert Einstein said: 'Imagination is more important than knowledge.' We must strive not just to extract the existing resources from the Earth, but to create new resources as well.

Chapter 6

THE BIOSPHERE

So far, we have talked about outer space, the atmosphere and the Earth. Our focus has been on human beings—the space explorations we have undertaken and our use of space technologies, our mining of Earth and oceanic resources, and future technologies that can benefit us. Our discussions have revolved largely around the resources that can be economically useful to mankind. This is only natural, since in the history of evolution, the superior species have always tried to shape their surroundings to best suit the welfare and progress of their own species.

But the uniqueness of human beings is in their ability to understand the processes of nature through a variety of knowledge methodologies, one of the most powerful being scientific knowledge. Technology, the sibling of science, gives human beings the ability to use the scientific knowledge they have acquired to create new tools or processes to speed up many of the 'slow' processes of nature, and to create new products. The bulk of the discoveries and innovations effected during the twentieth century have sped up the process of change in a way that is unprecedented in the Earth's history. The human population has been increasing rapidly—while in earlier periods the human population would double itself over several millennia, it now does so in a matter of decades. Human per capita consumption of most resources (e.g. energy, water and food) has not only increased manifold over the last century but has diversified to cover many possible sources. Human beings have created over 3,000 new species through the cultivation of plants, the domestication of animals and the knowledge of cross-breeding. Over the past few decades, the knowledge of genomes has empowered humans to create many genetically modified (GM) seeds and vegetables.

But these human-centric approaches of the past centuries— which were perhaps vital for human progress—have now created a situation where, due to speedy utilization of natural resources, there are fears of the Earth heating up beyond tolerable limits, leading to irreversible climate change. Increasingly, there is now a sharp awareness of the close interconnectedness between human beings and nature, and all living beings are seen as part of a systemic whole that is in harmony with the inanimate world of the Earth, the oceans and the atmosphere. If not for philosophical or ethical reasons, such a world view is now crucial for the very survival of human beings. It is therefore important for us to learn about the biosphere, of which we are a very small part.

The term 'biosphere' was coined by Vladimir Vernadsky, a Russian scientist. It means 'life zone of the Earth', which includes all living organisms and organic matter. It is thus meant to refer to any part where some life form is present, including land, water and the air. All parts of the Earth covered by layers of water or ice (usually called the hydrosphere), the layers of the atmosphere that envelop the Earth, and the soil are together referred to as the biosphere.

The primordial soup

When the Earth was spun off from the Sun there was no biosphere. The beginnings of the biosphere was around 4,500 million years ago with the onset of what geologists describe as the Pre-Cambrian period, when the continents were formed. The atmosphere was also formed around this time, but it was not like the atmosphere we have today. The atmosphere then was a thin envelope of hydrogen, carbon dioxide, ammonia and methane. It contained no free oxygen which is crucial to life (and therefore called *pranavaayu* or 'air of life' in Sanskrit). Over a period of time, that is, many millions of years, water vapour condensed to form seas of very hot waters. As if these were not enough, massive volcanic eruptions from the hot internal layers of the Earth spewed lava and ash on the surface of the Earth including the hot seas. Even outer space was not kind to Earth; since the atmosphere was very thin, ultraviolet rays were showered harshly on the newly formed planet. It is quite incredible that this hostile environment became the home for the origin of life. But that only shows us how remarkable and even unpredictable the processes of nature can be.

The same hostile conditions—harsh ultraviolet rays and electrical charges from lightning acting on the gases in the thin atmosphere and the water vapour enveloping the primordial Earth—produced complex molecules such as sugars, lipids, nucleic acids and amino acids through a process now called chemical synthesis. Millions of years passed by while more and more of these complex molecules were created and their concentration grew steadily. These complex molecules also started interacting with each other, creating other new complex molecules. Their concentration reached a stage that scientists now call a 'primordial soup' (Darwin liked a fonder expression—'warm little pond').*

The reactions (synthesis and cross-linkages) led to the formation of nucleotides. Many such nucleotides join together to form one strand of nucleic acid. Among the great variety of substances that were formed, one substance called deoxyribonucleic acid (DNA) made a major difference. This was because DNA could (as it continues to do now) replicate itself. It does not have to wait for a new chemical synthesis to take place in the primordial soup but can keep making copies of itself over and over again on its own.

---

*For more information please see the Vigyan Prasar books *Life on Earth* by Sukanya Datta and *Planet Earth in a Nutshell* by Biman Basu; some of the information in this chapter is drawn from these books.

Each of the new DNA strands is again able to replicate itself. Not only that, DNA also serves as a blueprint for the manufacture of amino acids, the simplest form of proteins.

The stage was thus set in that hostile environment for early life or microorganisms to appear on Earth. A series of steps led to the formation of cells, which are the basic building blocks of life.

Had the DNA been replicating itself in perfect copies, the Earth would have just been filled up by standardized DNA and amino acid strands, with no variation whatsoever. This sameness would make further evolution virtually impossible. But in the process of replication, some 'errors' were introduced in some of the replicated DNA. These errors replicated themselves in turn and produced entirely new strands of DNA that went on to create totally different proteins. As a result, it became possible for there to be several variations of proteins and the process of evolutionary natural selection, which involves the 'survival of the fittest' and future sustainability of the group preferred by nature, could take place. If there is no diversity, there is no opportunity for selection. Without options, there is little scope for betterment; with sameness, stasis reigns, and evolution becomes impossible.

Life arrives on Earth

Through this process of diversity and selection, cells appeared on Earth about 1,200 millions years ago. Around that time, the first single-celled organisms known as prokaryotes (ancestors of present-day bacteria) came into existence. This was part of a time during which the amount of atmospheric oxygen increased, and made life on Earth sustainable. Geologists call this era the Pre-Cambrian period (4500–570 million years ago). During the later part of this period, organisms known as eukaryotes, possessing a cellular nucleus and nuclear membrane, appeared. Simple plants and invertebrate animals—algae, bacteria, jelly fish, flagellates, amoebas, worms and sponges—began to appear. These exist even now, though some of them have evolved into higher organisms.

Paleozoic era: The next period of time, after life arrived, is called the Paleozoic era (570–250 million years ago) by geologists. It has several specialized periods.

- Cambrian period (570–500 million years ago): Multi-cellular life starts proliferating on a major scale. Trilobites, brachiopods, clams, snails, crustaceans, gastropods, corals, protzoans appear.
- Ordovician period (500–438 million years ago): Primitive life appears on land—an important landmark. Vertebrates appear in the oceans (precursors of many fishes).
- Silwian period (438–408 million years ago): First plants and insects appear on land. Sharks, bony fish and scorpions appear.
- Devonian period (408–360 million years ago): Spiders, mites and amphibians appear.
- Carboniferous period (360–286 million years ago): The first true reptiles appear. Coal begins to form.
- Permian period (286–250 million years ago): This was more a period of destruction for many life forms. Mass extinction took place and 90 per cent of all organisms evolved so far died out. But even amidst this large-scale destruction, reptiles with large sail-like fins appear.

Mesozoic era: The next block of time is known as the Mesozoic era (260–65 millions years ago). It is again subdivided into several periods.

- Triassic period (250–205 million years ago): Cycads (tropical trees somewhat like the palm trees of today) appear. Small dinosaurs appear. The first turtles, lizards and mammals appear.
- Jurassic period (205–138 million years ago): You may remember the name from the famous movie. This is when large dinosaurs, flying pterosaurs (the oldest known birds), the first squids, frogs and salamanders appear.

- Creataceous period (138–65 million years ago): Dinosaurs dominate the Earth. The first flowering plants, snakes and modern fish appear. Towards the end of this period, the dinosaurs are wiped out, probably as the result of an asteroid impact on Earth and the consequent fallout of debris.

Cenzoic era: The most recent era is the Cenzoic era (65 million years ago to the present). This is divided into periods and their subsets called epochs.

- Tertiary period (65–1.8 million years ago):

  i) Palacocene epoch (65–55.5 million years ago): Mammals inherit the Earth. Chief among the early mammals are marsupials, insectivores, lemuroids, creodonts (the carnivorous stock ancestral to all cats and dogs) and primitive hoofed animals.

  ii) Eocene epoch (55.5–33.7 million years ago): Ancestral forms of the horse, camel and other modern groups such as bats, primates, and squirrel-like rodents appear simultaneously in Europe and North America. Mammals adapt to marine life.

  iii) Oligocene epoch (33.7–23.8 million years ago): Elephants, cats, dogs, monkeys and great apes make their first appearance. First grasses appear.

  iv) Miocene epoch (23.8–5.3 million years ago): This is the period when a large-scale global cooling takes place. Ice sheets form in Antarctica. Raccoons and weasels make their first appearance. Large apes roam in Africa and Southern Europe. The first hominids (erect bipedal, two legged primates who are our ancestors) appear.

  v) Pleiocene epoch (5.3–1.8 million years ago): The Earth's climate becomes cooler and drier. Mammals establish themselves as the dominant terrestrial life form. It is during this period that the rapid evolution of one group, the primates, produces a species considered to be direct ancestors of modern humans.

- Quaternary period (1.8 million years ago to the present):

    i) Pleistocene epoch (1.8 million–8000 years ago): Most recent global ice age occurs. Glaciers spread over more than one-fourth of the Earth's land surface. Human beings take advantage of the ice age, which links the landmasses through the solid ice of the oceans, to begin their migrations.

    ii) Halocene epoch (8000 years ago to the present): The first modern human beings appear.

The many millions of years that this calendar of life deals with may sometimes be difficult to grasp in relation to human history, which is only a few thousand years old. In his book *Life on Earth*, the naturalist David Attenborough proposed a useful year-long calendar, starting with the beginning of life to the present, where 1 day = 10 million years. On such a calendar Man did not appear till the evening of 31 December! But with the appearance of Man on 31 December, things started moving very fast.

Human beings started affecting the biosphere in significant ways, not just for their survival but also for their convenience. Trees were cut down in large numbers for housing, farming and agriculture. Agriculture involved growing certain preferred plants over others on a large scale. As trading began, preferred plants and animals were brought together from diverse ecosystems around the world. Man also crossbred many plants and animals and created new species, modifying the existing ones. These species may have taken a few million years to evolve had human intervention not been there; perhaps some of them may not have been selected in the natural selection process. Large-scale agriculture and farming helped the human population to grow and prosper, soon making Man the dominant species on Earth.

This rapid change and expansion affected the biosphere in major ways. Human mining of coal and petroleum and their large-scale use; the artificial large-quantity production of many chemicals which occur in nature in small quantities; large-scale irrigation using artificially built dams and canals; large-scale destruction of forests to create human habitats—these have all affected the land, oceans and atmosphere on a scale that is noticeable. The extinction of some species of animals, birds and plants are a result, as is local atmospheric and water pollution. Severe changes in the global climate patterns are being noticed now and are causing deep concern. There are some who believe that life on Earth has now entered the Anthropocene epoch, where human-induced changes may cause great damage to the ecology of the Earth.

Biodiversity

One of the important strengths of the biosphere is its diversity. We have seen how the errors in the replication of DNAs led to diversity in the first place. That diversity is still the strength of nature and of life on Earth.

Why is biodiversity required? Is not natural selection, involving the survival of the fittest, already at work? Does it not decide which species are better equipped for survival and further replication? Why should we take the sides of some particular species, and try to save the so-called endangered species from dying out? Does the condition of millions of human beings suffering from poverty and malnourishment require more attention, or is an 'esoteric' concept like biodiversity more urgent?

These are questions that go through the minds of many people who worry about the large-scale poverty in India and in other parts of the world, and would like to see it eradicated. Eradication of poverty requires more and more development with steps such as the modernization of agriculture with high-yielding seed varieties such as hybrid and genetically modified (GM) seeds, and a concentration on high-value agriproducts; the growth of large-scale energy plantations that can supply biofuels; the reclamation of wastelands for industry and tourism; large-scale modifications to water bodies to make water available to all through modern engineering systems, and so on. But when these development plans are drawn up, the votaries of biodiversity often oppose them, saying that the plans would wreak havoc on ecological habitats and lead to the extinction of some plant and animal species. It is a constant tussle between the two lines of thought. So which one is right?

It is a natural human emotion to feel for our fellow creatures, whether it is a household pet or a garden plant, a creature of the wild or a tree in the forest. This is due in part perhaps to the interconnectedness between everything in nature. The diversity that nature propagates is also linked to interconnectedness. DNAs do not change drastically overnight. Development over millions of years effects only a small change, but the external appearances of that change makes one product of nature look very different from another. For instance, the DNA changes between human beings amounts to less than 1 per cent; yet an Indian looks very different from a Chinese, and a European from an African.

This commonality apart, even the prey and predator are linked in nature—in fact, they depend on each other to survive. The famous example given for interlinked population cycles is that of rabbits and foxes. When the rabbit population grows rapidly, foxes get more food and therefore their population increases too. That leads to a point when the foxes eat up so many rabbits that there is a decline in the rabbit population. This in turn leads to a decline in the fox population: many foxes die hungry, and many die without mating and reproduction. In effect, the rabbit and fox populations keep balancing each other. If the process is left to nature without major external disturbances, then through a series of such cycles an ecological balance is reached.

Nature has a way of balancing things. In the long history of evolution, there are periods when one species has tried to dominate. But in totality, nature manages to balance the ecosystem. It is not that no species affects nature. In fact, every living organism (unicellular or multicellular) does affect nature, because it draws resources from nature for its own living and reproduction, and destroys something in the process; in turn, while alive or dead, it provides food and/or energy to some other life form.

It is because of this interconnectedness and interdependence that human beings cannot take an imperious position and presume to decide on behalf of nature. All achievements that human beings may boast of are relevant only in the context of their lives on Earth, in relation to the environment and the biosphere. No doubt human beings are able to manipulate their environment in remarkable ways, much more than their size would suggest, since they are intelligent. But still, in spite of all the knowledge and technology that is at his/her command, no one can say that he/she knows everything there is to know about nature. As much as we know about nature through our researches, there are always a few elements unknown to us. Think about this, for instance: was any scientist able to predict the spread of HIV/AIDS or other new viral diseases that are now threatening to become widespread epidemics?

If human beings are smart, we should also recognize the simple scientific fact that billions of other species have at least some minimal capabilities to learn and to adapt. That is the reason they evolved and created organisms in the new evolutionary ladder. In medical reports when malaria breaks out or tuberculosis spreads, you often hear about drug-resistant varieties playing a deciding role. Human beings kill harmful viruses and bacteria with medicines; many die, but a few that survive learn how to combat the chemicals used by us against them, and then these strains multiply. Over a period of time they create new drug-resistant varieties and attack us again, more powerfully than before.

When modern science and technology were growing rapidly

during the nineteenth and twentieth centuries, it is understandable that scientists, philosophers and others thought all solutions to the well being of human beings could be obtained through science and its applications. They felt that all answers regarding life on Earth would be available through science. But experience has shown that it is not so. No doubt science, technology and economic systems have helped human beings a lot. Solutions have even been found to difficult ecological puzzles like atmospheric pollution and water pollution. But the more our knowledge grows, the more we discover new questions for which answers have to be found.

The complexity, interconnectedness and interdependence of everything in nature is clearly understood through scientific processes. Not that we know all the linkages, but we do understand that everything is interconnected. This understanding is crucial to the way forward, because it teaches us that human beings must not take unilateral decisions that would upset the patterns and processes of nature. Biodiversity is all about understanding, respecting and maintaining the rich diversity in nature.

A report by the Office of Technology Assessment (OTA) of the US Congress from 1988, titled 'Technologies to Maintain Biological Diversity', articulates the current thoughts on biodiversity succinctly.

> Biological diversity refers to the variety and variability among living organisms and the ecological complexes in which they occur. Diversity can be defined as the number of different items and their relative frequency. For biological diversity, these items are organized at many levels, ranging from complete ecosystems to the chemical structures that are the molecular basis of heredity. Thus, the term encompasses different ecosystems, species, genes and their relative abundance.
>
> How does diversity vary within ecosystems, species and genetic levels? For example,
>
> • Ecosystem diversity: A landscape interspersed with croplands, grasslands and woodlands has more diversity than a landscape with most of the woodlands converted to grasslands and croplands.

- Species diversity: A rangeland with 100 species of annual and perennial grasses and shrubs has more diversity than the same rangeland after heavy grazing has eliminated or greatly reduced the frequency of the perennial grass species.
- Genetic diversity: Economically useful crops are developed from wild plants by selecting valuable inheritable characteristics. Thus, many wild ancestor plants contain genes not found in today's crop plants. An environment that includes both the domestic varieties of a crop (such as corn) and the crop's wild ancestors has more diversity than an environment with wild ancestors eliminated to make way for domestic crops.

Concerns over the loss of biological diversity to date have been defined almost exclusively in terms of species extinction. Although extinction is perhaps the most dramatic aspect of the problem, it is by no means the whole problem. The consequence is a distorted definition of the problem, which fails to account for many of the interests concerned and may misdirect how concerns should be addressed.

The loss of diversity at the three levels (ecosystem, species and genetic) is mainly because of the human interventions in and modifications to the natural landscape, human selection of certain species by its preference for commercial reasons. These in turn reduce genetic diversity. For example, human beings may prefer certain high-yielding seeds or animals and protect and replicate them more for their commercial use. Modified landscapes may kill many insects, worms and even larger animals (the loss of tiger and lion populations is due to the intrusion of humans into forests thus changing the natural landscape there). The need for diversity is not merely because of compassion or kindness alone. There is also the scientific aspect of respecting the interdependence within an ecosystem, though we may not know all the connections, linkages and causative factors.

There is another dimension to the need for biodiversity which is brought out in the OTA report.

Loss of biodiversity may eliminate options to use untapped resources for agricultural, industrial and medicinal development. Crop genetic resources have accounted for about 50 per cent of productivity increases and for annual contributions of about $1 billion to US agriculture. For instance, two species of wild green tomatoes discovered in an isolated area of the Peruvian highlands in the early 1960s have contributed genes for marked increase in fruit pigmentation and soluble–solids content currently worth nearly $5 million per year to the tomato-processing industry. Future gains will depend on use of genetic diversity.

Loss of plant species could mean loss of billions of dollars in potential plant-derived pharmaceutical products. About 25 per cent of the number of prescription drugs in the United States are derived from plants. In 1980, their total market value was $8 billion. Loss of tropical rainforests, which harbour an extraordinary diversity of species, and loss of deserts, which harbour genetically diverse vegetation, are of particular concern. Consequences to humans of loss of potential medicines have impacts that go beyond economic benefits. Alkaloids from the rosy periwinkle (*catharantus roseus*), a tropical plant, for example, are used in the successful treatment of several forms of cancer, including Hodgkin's disease and childhood leukemia.

Although research in biotechnology suggests exciting prospects, scientists will continue to rely on genetic resources crafted by nature. For example, new methods of manipulating genetic material enable the isolation and extraction of a desired gene from one plant or organism and its insertion into another. Nature provides the basic materials; science enables the merging of desired properties into new forms or combinations. Loss of diversity, therefore, may undermine society's realization of the technology's potential.

With the rapid growth of life sciences and biotechnology, human beings will know more about ways to maintain biodiversity and enhance it marginally. But let us not fool ourselves into a belief that we may be able to recreate many of the lost ecosystems, species and genes through our biotechnological knowledge. As the OTA report states:

This report assesses the potential of diversity maintenance technologies and the institutions developing and applying these technologies. But maintaining biological diversity will depend on more than applying technologies. Technologies do not exist to re-create the vast majority of ecosystems, species, and genes that are being lost, and there is little hope that such technologies will be developed in the foreseeable future. Therefore, efforts to maintain diversity must also address the socioeconomic, political and cultural factors involved.

There are a whole set of scientific methodologies and technologies available now to help maintain biodiversity. But none of them will really yield the desired results without the active awareness and participation of all human beings, from little children to the elderly. Conservation of biodiversity cannot be a responsibility that is left any longer at someone else's doorstep, be it the government or the environment department or activists or science laboratories or national parks. All of us have to act.

But in order to act intelligently, we need to understand a few fundamentals. We cannot just talk about nature's diversity and be overwhelmed by the number of species there are and new discoveries which our researchers are making. Scientific understanding requires a systematic and methodological arrangement of the observations we make. So let us look at some basic classifications of life forms and organisms on Earth.

Classifications

The Swedish biologist Carolus Linnaeus, in 1735, created a methodology for the classification of animals and plants. He grouped everything under the Animal, Vegetable and Mineral kingdoms. Each species is designated by a two-word name. The first word is the generic name of the species and the second the specific name (for example, humans are the species *Homo sapiens*). The science of classification or taxonomy helps to look for anatomical features that appear to have the same function as those found in other species. The specificities of each species are noted. That is how the two-word classification is done.

In the hierarchical system of classification the highest category is the kingdom. At this level, organisms are identified on the basis of cellular organization and methods of nutrition. Since much better instruments than the simple microscopes of the past are available now, there are more kingdoms than the original three that have been identified:

- Kingdom Animalia: Multi-cellular mobile organisms that cannot synthesize their own food but depend on others.
- Kingdom Plantae: Organisms that can make their own food. Examples include all green plants.
- Kingdom Protists: Organisms that have single, complex cells. Examples include protozoa and single-celled algae.
- Kingdom Fungi: Organisms that absorb food from living and non-living things. Examples include yeasts.
- Kingdom Monera: Organisms that have single, simple cells. Examples are bacteria and blue-green algae.

Food and energy

It is important to remember that whether big or small, simple or complex, no organism lives alone. It is through food that energy flows from one species to another. The green plants use sunlight to synthesize their own food; they are at the base of the food chain. Some animals (herbivores) eat plants and derive their energy from these. Some animals (carnivores) eat other animals and get their energy from them.

It is interesting to note that in the food chain, an animal passes on only about 10 per cent of the energy it receives. About 90 per cent of the potential energy is lost as heat. So further along the food chain, the energy that is passed on becomes very low. An animal eating another animal loses a lot of energy. The shorter the food chain, the more efficient it is. If we eat plants, we use energy more efficiently. In future, human beings will have to ponder over this reality, when they make a choice between eating vegetables and meat.

The food chain is made up of:

- Primary producers (plants)
- Primary consumers (herbivores)
- Secondary consumers (carnivores)
- Tertiary consumers (carnivores eating carnivores)
- Decomposers (fungi)

The decomposed chemicals go back to the earth and from there to the plants, and so the cycle continues.

Organisms are also classified by trophic levels: those whose food is obtained from plants (which are the source of food for all life) by the same number of steps belong to the same trophic level. So green plants, being the primary producers, belong to the first trophic level, herbivores to the second trophic level, carnivores that eat only herbivores to the third, and carnivores that eat other carnivores to the fourth. Of course, a species may occupy more than one trophic level. For instance, omnivores like humans occupy the second, third and fourth trophic levels.

The trophic structure is usually shown by three ecological pyramids.

- Pyramid of numbers: This depicts the number of individuals at each level.
- Pyramid of biomass: This is based on the total mass of organisms (number of individuals multiplied by their weight) at each trophic level.
- Pyramid of energy: This depicts feeding and other relationships within a food chain or web.

Biogeochemical cycles

Another important aspect crucial for ecological understanding concerns the biogeochemical cycles of the Earth. For all practical purposes the Earth is a closed system for matter. In other words, all matter on Earth has to be transformed from the existing matter;

nothing new is available from elsewhere (except for very tiny quantities of cosmic dust which falls on Earth). Therefore the elements of matter which were formed billions of years ago become the basic ingredients for anything new that is to be created. It was from these that the basic components of the first life forms came. Matter continually cycles through Earth, becoming food, becoming energy. These cycles can last a few days or millions of years. There are different pathways, different sources, different resting places where these elements may rest before changing into something else. These cycles are collectively called biogeochemical cycles and exist throughout the biosphere. Those essential to life are called 'nutrient cycles'. The most important biogeochemical cycles are those of water, carbon and nitrogen.

With the arrival of Homo sapiens with their advanced knowledge, many of these cycles which had their own pace and intensity have been seriously altered. For example, the human use of fertilizers on a large scale (which is needed to sustain the food supply for a huge and fast-growing human population) has altered the natural nitrogen and phosphorous cycles. Excessive amounts of these elements from the 'waste' agricultural water go into water bodies and overfertilize them; the entire aquatic biosystem is affected as a result.

Actions for the immediate future

In the coming years it is essential to understand how natural cycles have been seriously altered by human actions and to try to reduce their effects—perhaps through large-scale local recycling and reuse of all forms of wastes. Residual chemical and biological wastes may have to be treated separately.

Similarly, while near-term commercial considerations may make us use certain specific high-yielding grains or animals or poultry for our food consumptions, we may need to create large-scale genetic banks to preserve many other varieties (of rice, wheat, corn, fruits or flowers or even of pigs and cattle), so that genetic diversities and species diversities are preserved. As shown in certain examples of biodiversity before, some of these may turn out to be economically important later. Sometimes one has to resort to some of these genetic or species varieties to save many resources from pandemic viral attacks. So there is a utilitarian aspect to the preservation of biodiversity as well.

In addition, ecosystem biodiversities need to be preserved and proactively protected as well, for the healthy future of the planet.

All this will require much more knowledge about the biosphere, biodiversity, the ecosystem, and the Earth in general. The scientific approach today is becoming much more holistic and inclusive than it was before. The twenty-first century is thus going to be a period of realizing and recovering the glories of nature through scientific methods and also mining the knowledge bases of the civilizational heritage of the past as well as current living traditions. India is fortunate to have many such living traditions that connect human beings to nature.

At an address delivered at the Regional Research Laboratory at Jammu on 26 June 2003, this is what Dr Kalam had to say about biodiversity in India.

India is blessed with more than sixteen bio-climates which enable us to produce a variety of herbal plants. A happy combination of modern biotechnology with the rich natural diversity could produce good results that will extend far beyond the borders of this state.

One of the core competences of India is biodiversity. Biodiversity and technology combined will yield value-added products. In biodiversity, only a few countries like India, China, Brazil, Indonesia and Mexico are very rich. Technology is needed to develop a genetically engineered seed or to transform a molecule extracted from the herb into a drug. The technologically advanced nations in this field are the USA, UK, Japan, France and Germany. Today there is no nation that is rich in biodiversity and also technologically advanced in the area. There are some desert nations where both biodiversity and technology are poor. Therefore the challenge for India is the integration of the best of technology and the abundant biodiversity. What is needed is an integration of high productivity in farming, biodiversity material and technology.

India is rich in herbs, germ plasm and microorganisms. Industrially developed countries import these bio-resources in the raw form and add value to them for export to developing countries including India as special seeds, medicines and bio-materials, fully protecting the patents of these products. Instead of allowing export of such resources and importing value-added products at high cost, India must add its own technology for conversion of such resources to value-added products for use in domestic requirement and also for export.

LIFE

Chapter 7

FOOD

Food is the sustainer of life. For all living organisms there are four essential aspects of life: to be born, to eat, to reproduce, and to die. Food is what provides energy to living beings, so it is essential for survival and growth. Accordingly, all life forms spend a large part of their lives on the acquisition of food.

Those of us who have an assured supply of food on our tables, and can go out and buy more anytime in the cooked form or as raw ingredients, seldom think about where the food comes from and the effort it takes to produce it. The commercial food market and the advertisements focus only on the finished, packaged food products, not on the process through which these come into being. In most middle class families, the parents ensure that there is sufficient food available for everybody and put on the table on time. In fact, food is so plentiful for the well-to-do that children often refuse to eat, and have to be chased after to be fed! On the other hand, much of the malnourished and undernourished population, chronically deprived of food, is not able to digest and process food even if it is made available.

The steady availability of nutritious food is essential for human beings. Enough calories to provide energy do not make up a nutritious diet in themselves; our food intake must have a good balance of proteins, fats and carbohydrates, with sufficient minerals and vitamins, and enough water. We also need some roughage (fibres) in our diet: this aids digestion and eases defecation. In addition roughage and curd are also the habitats of many beneficial bacteria.

We should remember that the human body is not made up of cells, water, and other chemicals alone. There are many microbes (mostly bacteria), almost 10,000 times more in number than human cells, which live in every human body. Our first reaction to the word 'bacteria' is to find a way of getting rid of them. But it is not possible to get rid of all the bacteria that live inside us; in fact, if we did so, our own cells would be seriously affected. Many of these microbes perform useful functions such as helping break down food to forms that can be easily absorbed by the body. No doubt some of these microbes can also cause various illnesses; the body's immune system has to learn to fight with dangerous microbes. Microbes are everywhere on Earth and in the atmosphere. They are part of the biosystem that we have discussed in the previous chapter.

Evolution of food habits

The evolution of the human alimentary system over millions of years has conditioned our food habits in very particular ways. Some evolutionary theorists and experimenters now believe that humans were evolutionarily conditioned to discover (or invent) cooking. The human digestive system is not conducive to raw vegetarian food and cellulosic material alone (as is the case with many herbivores); it is also not suited to the consumption of purely carnivorous food (raw flesh). Cooked food increases the absorption of nutrients in the body. The cooking of food and thus reducing the quantity that needs to be eaten provided food security to humans and allowed the human body to grow faster; it also put Man in an advantageous position in relation to other species.

A quick look at the nutritional history of human beings over the different phases of development, along with a listing of the various types of nutritional disorders we have had, will be interesting.*

Hunter–gatherers: More than 10,000 years ago, before agriculture was invented by humans, our ancestors were hunter–gatherers. They hunted wild animals and birds for food and gathered a wide range of fruits, roots, leaves etc. to supplement their diet. Today we know of hunter–gatherers only as parts of isolated tribes in small pockets of the world. The hunter–gatherers' diet did not include salt, milk or sugar (except for wild honey). They had very little cereals (only what was available in their wild form).

The hunter–gatherers had a tough life. Their nutritional state was as follows:

- They were lean (no obesity at all)
- Malnutrition was unlikely
- There were no coronary diseases, no hypertension
- They had no dental cavities
- There was no alcoholism.

Pastoralists: After the hunter–gatherers came humans who had domesticated large populations of animals (cattle) and followed them in search of places where there would be large grazing pastures. Some Tibetans, Mongols, Tuareg, Fulani and Masai are pastoralists even today. In regions that are developed (including India), pastoralists have disappeared due to the paucity of available land. Those who tend cattle are now part of the organized agricultural system.

The pastoralists depended largely on animal food and milk. Their nutritional state was as follows:

- Some groups were tall
- There was a persistence of adult intestinal lactase.

---

*We have drawn on Davidsons' *Principles and Practice of Medicine* (seventeenth edition) edited by C.R.W. Edwards et al, for this information.

Peasant agriculturists: About 10,000 years ago, our ancestors became farmers. Even today, in most of the developing countries including India and also in some industrialized countries, we will find large populations of farmers and farm labourers.

Agriculturists are mostly rural people who often tend to depend upon the cultivation of one crop that yields the best and can sell easily in the market. As a result, they are vulnerable to crop diseases, crop toxins and droughts. They also suffer from seasonal shortages, pest attacks etc. Since milling and refining of cereals have become common due to the easy availability of machines, there is an increasing risk of malnutrition due to the loss of husk and roughage.

The nutritional state of peasant agriculturists is as follows:

- Malnutrition due to the loss of nutrients
- Vulnerability to food shortages due to vagaries of rainfall, pests etc.
- Illness due to toxins from agricultural practices.

Urban slum and periurban shanty dwellers: These are the masses of poor people who live in and around the fast-growing metros. The deplorable living conditions of slum dwellers were described even in the nineteenth century by writers such as Charles Dickens. Those who live in these conditions mostly lose their own food traditions. They suffer from the chronic paucity of food, poor quality of food and poor food hygiene.

Nutritional disorders are seen most among this group of people, who are in large numbers around the world, with India alone being home to a few hundred million.

- Chronic undernourishment and malnutrition
- Children are the most vulnerable, with mother's milk in short supply and with the unavailability of good substitutes. They suffer from gastroenteritis and other diseases
- Unbalanced and improper diets
- Alcoholism amongst adults.

Affluent societies: This group of people have no shortage of food. With their high purchasing power, the seasonality of food ceases to matter, as they are able to afford their favourite foods throughout the year. Most of the food they eat is highly processed and have a high fat and starch content. They experiment with alternate and unorthodox foods, often as a fashion statement. They also take many food supplements and vitamins.

Some of the characteristics of the nutritional state of modern affluent citizens are:

- Malnutrition is rare, but hospitalization due to eating disorders is common
- Coronary heart disease, diabetes, hypertension and other ailments are common
- Individuals suffer from obesity on the one hand and also emaciation because of anorexia on the other
- Insufficient exercise and lifestyle defects lead to other health problems.

It is clear that while food production has increased dramatically over the past century, dietary patterns and the distribution of available food leave a lot to be desired. In India today, we have only the last three categories of people discussed above—agriculturalists, poor slum dwellers and the urban rich. But we have a lot to learn from the food habits of the hunter–gatherers and pastoralists as well. Human beings may still be carrying a genetic diversity in their bodies and the uniformization of their food through modern mass manufactured brands may not be conducive to their growth and well being.

We will now discuss the availability of food for people in all three categories. The basic foundations of food availability are constituted by crops, vegetables, fruits, animal flesh and fish. These are interdependent segments. Animal husbandry has direct links to the growth of crops, especially in the present-day commercial methods of production, and vice versa.*

Crops and cultivation

During 1943, India suffered a major famine known as the Bengal famine. Independence came soon after and a precarious food situation resulting from the severe dislocations due to Partition followed. Agricultural development was given priority in the first Five-Year Plan starting 1950. Efforts towards building big dams like the Bhakra dam, which would aid irrigation, also began.

India started importing wheat from the USA to keep its food supply going. Seeing the terrible situation, wittily called a 'ship-to-mouth existence', of the nation's food supplies, C. Subramanian, the father of the Green Revolution, started schemes for using Norman Borlaug's technology for high-yielding food grains. This process began around 1968.

At the time, Americans were predicting widespread famine in India in the 1970s. About 25 per cent of the American wheat crop was being consumed by India, and they projected that the increasing demand could not be met by available supplies. But in 1975, thanks to the Green Revolution, India not only met the domestic requirement of food but also became a net exporter of food grains.

The following table provides a clear overview of India's current agricultural situation:

---

*Much of the information that follows is drawn from the twenty-seven volume report of the Ministry of Agriculture, Government of India, published in 2004, entitled *State of the Indian Farmer: A Millennium Study*.

India's Position in World Agriculture in 1998

	Item	India	World	% Share	Rank	Next to
1	Area (Mn.Hec.)					
	Total Area	329	13387	2.5	7	Canada, USA, China, Brazil
	Land Area	297	13048	2.3	7	USA, China, Canada, Brazil
	Arable Land	162F	1379	11.8	2	USA
	Irrigated Area	57F	268	21.3	1	
2	Population (Mn)					
	Total	982	5901	16.6	2	China
	Agriculture	549	2565	21.4	2	China
3	Economically Active Population (Mn)					
	Total	429	2865	15.0	2	China
	Agriculture	260	1308	19.9	2	China
4	Crop Production (MT)					
	A. Total Cereals	219	2054	10.7	3	China, USA
	Wheat	66	589	11.2	2	China
	Rice (Paddy)	122	563	21.6	2	China
	Coarse Grains	31	902	3.4	3	USA, China
	B. Total Pulses	14 F	57	24.6	1	
	Oilseeds					
	Groundnut	8	31	25.8	2	China
	Rapeseed	5	34	14.7	3	Canada, China
5	Fruits & Vegetables(MT)					
	A. Vegetables & Melon	56F	606	9.2	2	China

Item	India	World	% Share	Rank	Next to
B. Potato	25F	296	8.5	4	China, Russian Federation, Poland
C. Onion (Dry)	4F	40	10.0	2	China
6 Commercial Crops (MT)					
A. Sugarcane	265	1252	21.2	2	Brazil
B. Tea	0.87	2.96	29.4	1	
C. Coffee (Green)	0.23	6.46	3.6	7	Brazil, Colombia, Indonesia, Mexico
D. Tobacco Leaves	0.64	7.06	9.1	3	China, USA

Source: State of the Indian Farmer: A Millennium Study (2004), Report 9.

India is among the top ten countries in the world in most crop production activities. India is one of the largest producers of food grains but also one of the largest consumers. The consumption has kept increasing due to the continued and speedy growth of India's population since Independence.

Farmers in India comprise about 20 per cent of the global farming population. But India's total size of farmlands is small in comparison. Hence the density of farming is very high, i.e. many more farmers tend to work in a small area. Another feature of agriculture in India is that the farm economy is largely food crop based, while about 25 per cent of the area is used for commercial crop production. Thus farmers' incomes are low, since financial returns from food grains are lower.

Only in three of the twenty-two items listed in the table above does India rank first. Though in total amount of arable land we are second to the USA, in terms of percentage of arable land compared to the total land area, India is at the top; this is because most of our land has excellent arable soil. There is scope for us to achieve much more because our soil is good, the climate conducive, and a large area of arable land (55 per cent of the total land) is available. We should be glad to note that we are number one in terms of total irrigated area. But our crop production is not commensurate with our ranking because we do not use water efficiently. We need to use modern technologies of spray-and-drip irrigation instead of the centuries-old system of flood irrigation. In Israel 80 per cent of water used for agriculture is recycled. If we can also achieve similar figures in recycling and use water conservation technologies, we can have every Indian farm irrigated using the same amount of water that we do today. In fact we will have surplus water to use for industrial and domestic ecological rejuvenation purposes.

About 56 per cent of our population depends on agriculture for their livelihood. About 60 per cent of the active work force is in the agriculture sector. But seeing that agriculture contributes less than 20 per cent of our total GDP, this 60 per cent produces much less in monetary terms than the average Indian working in other fields, and has a lower income too. Partly this is due to the fact that agricultural prices are kept down by government policies. But even if the prices were raised, there would be repercussions such as the vicious cycle of inflation. Therefore there is a need to decrease the number of persons working in the agriculture sector in order to remove their poverty. This means the use of technologically upgraded and science-based inputs to increase productivity.

India's total production of food grains, as shown in the table dating back to 1998, is 219 million tonnes. Even with the population shown as 982 million, per capita availability of food grains per year is (219 ÷ 982) x 1000 = 223 kg (1 tonne = 1000 kg). India's current population is around 1,160 million, but the food grain production is still hovering around 220 million tonnes.

Comprehensive analyses done by the late Prof. S.K. Sinha, a great agricultural scientist who led the Technology Vision 2020 exercise in agriculture and food at the Technology Information, Forecasting and Assessment Council (TIFAC), indicate that the present per capita availability of food grains will be inadequate for India as economic growth takes place. At the same time, Sinha rejects the doomsday scenario projected by foreign agencies which assume that per capita consumption of food grains in India will rise to European or American standards. At this point, a closer understanding of food grain consumption is required.

In the previous chapter, we have seen how it is more difficult to obtain energy from flesh than from grains and vegetables. People in developed regions like Europe and the USA consume more meat, poultry and dairy products, and less food grains. Food grains are fed mostly to animals and birds and their flesh is then eaten. The energy conversion efficiency in this process is low. If one has to derive from cattle meat the equivalent energy that can be derived from directly eating one portion of food grains, the animal needs to consume almost ten times that amount of food grains to provide the equivalent amount of meat. For pork, mutton etc. the ratio is about 5:1, and for poultry it is about 2:1. In India, the direct consumption of food grains by humans is much higher, and therefore the same amount of energy can be derived from a much lower total consumption of food grains. Of course, this leads to other dietary imbalances, but that is a separate concern.

International agencies project a similar pattern to that which exists in Europe and the USA for Indian food consumption in the future, and come to the conclusion that with a population of about 1.4 billion people around 2020, India would have a sharp food scarcity and would have to import food. This is a projection that is made in ignorance of the ground realities in India. As part of their visions exercise on agriculture and food, Prof. Sinha and his team looked at changes in food patterns for those who have become relatively affluent in India. Though a large section of Indians are non-vegetarians, there are many variations amongst this segment. Even a non-vegetarian in India may not eat any meat for many days in a year due to cultural and religious reasons. Also when Indians become affluent, their consumption of vegetables and fruits goes up, thus reducing the intake of direct food grains. Taking all these factors into account Prof. Sinha concluded that if production of food grains in India reached around 360 million tonnes, not only would the domestic needs be taken care of, but there would also be some surplus grain to export.

The good agro-climatic conditions India is blessed with and the large amount of arable land that we have should have continued to boost agricultural production in India even after the Green Revolution. But as we have seen, food grain production has hit a plateau. Look at the production of pulses for example. Though India is the top producer of pulses in the world, we still have to import pulses to meet our consumption needs. Dal is a part of the food culture in just about every part of the country. So there is a need to step up the production of pulses as this can give better returns to the farmer, if he is backed by the right technologies and infrastructure.

A number of experiments undertaken as part of TIFAC's Vision 2020 projects in fourteen geographical areas since 1997 (in which Dr Kalam was also associated as chairman of TIFAC and Y.S. Rajan as Executive Director) definitely prove that even without a major push like the Green Revolution, our farmers are willing to learn new techniques and adapt to new technology–market–business linkages. They are also keen to spread technological information among other farmers by sharing the knowledge and skills acquired through their experience. But a sustained initiative to support such a movement is lacking on the part of government institutions at a district level.

Overall, Central government interventions followed by or partnered by state government initiatives were useful to launch the Green Revolution which removed the spectre of famine from India. But the benefits of the Green Revolution have been uneven. It has been a general trend in India that middle level farmers are the most adventurous in adopting new systems. Once they show the benefits and also help the whole system through the initial teething troubles, the rich farmers step in. They have more financial clout and other resources, and reap the maximum benefits. The marginal farmers are not ignorant of technology and its benefits but their ability to take risks is very low. Only when most of the rich and middle level farmers are well placed in the new system, the standard operations allow for lower cost access by the marginal farmers. This is what happened in Punjab and Haryana about two decades after the initial launch of the Green Revolution. But some parts of India did not get the full benefits of the Green Revolution, since some of the key elements, not just vital ingredients like seeds but access to irrigation, fertilizers, pesticides, road infrastructure and finance, did not reach them.

There is an extensive discussion of the spread of the benefits of the Green Revolution over the past few decades in the *State of the Indian Farmer* Report.

> There were 222 low productivity districts in India in 1960–63; this number came down by 1990–93. Only 4.4 per cent of the districts from the northwestern region and 13 per cent of the southern region districts continued as low productivity districts, whereas about two-thirds of the districts from the central region and one-third of the districts from the eastern region continued as low productivity districts. More than one-fourth of the districts in the states of Jammu and Kashmir, Bihar, Gujarat, Madhya Pradesh, Maharashtra, Rajasthan and Karnataka continued to be low productivity districts in the post-Green Revolution period.

Thus the Green Revolution clearly helped a large number of regions and farmers in those regions. But there are still significant areas (about 15 per cent of the total area of low productivity agriculture) that have not benefited as much. There is a need to look closely at these areas and see how the benefits of technology might reach them. Perhaps the focus here needs to be on a number of grains (including pulses and coarse grains) which have not been given sufficient attention so far.

The overall lessons learnt from the implementation of the Green Revolution are summarized in Report 9.

Our analysis indicates the following important aspects:

The crops which have taken quick advantage of the technology in the initial phase of the Green Revolution are likely to slow down. These crops are generally grown by medium and large farmers. It is only lately that the small and marginal farmers have adopted the high productivity, high value crop pattern and therefore productivity trends for these crops have to be watched. Increasing cost of cultivation of the crops may put the small and marginal farmers in a difficult situation in case of crop failures.

Slow growth crops have been identified here and these require significant attention in terms of location-specific technology. These crops are grown mainly by the weaker sections and subsistence farmers among the farming community and therefore have a telling effect on poverty.

Pulses have not been picking up in their growth performance despite various interventions and increasing price trends. The pulses along with coarse cereals require a fresh look from a technological viewpoint. The resourceful farmers are adopting the technology at the first instance but drop out after gaining some experience. The rest of the farmers' groups follow. Therefore, the distribution of grains will be truncated at the beginning but gets corrected in due course. However, this has temporarily an adverse impact on the poverty calculus.

Oilseeds had shown promising trends during the eighties but the Brown (oilseed) Revolution slowed down due to the lack of technological back-up and trade scenario. Some of the oilseed crops showed significantly declining trends in productivity during the nineties and the distress of oilseed growers was quite visible encompassing small and marginal farmers.

There are certain districts which have been consistently lagging behind in the crop economy right from Independence. They have been non-performers then and even now after five decades of efforts. Naturally, poverty is located intensively in these districts and the farmers are at a disadvantaged position.

One should not get the impression that the Central or state governments did not do anything for the benefit of the agricultural sector beyond the Green Revolution and its extensions over the past few decades. There were many Central schemes which were implemented to address various problems like the stagnation of productivity after the initial increase. They have had mixed results. Current crises on the agriculture front (with many farmers' suicides being reported) have to do with inadequacies in some of these new schemes. Also due to globalization and new World Trade Organization (WTO) directives, new forms of market forces are now acting on the agricultural sector and on farmers. In the earlier forms of low productivity agriculture, farmers had a good degree of self-sufficiency. But with the newer system a farmer has to depend upon external inputs every step of the way, right from the seed level onwards. The newer solutions cannot be based on science and technology alone; they require a multidimensional approach.

The findings of the Millennium Study are vital for the future food security of the country. It is clear that there is a need for continued R&D and extension services in the agriculture sector. Pest-resistant varieties of crops are grown through intensive R&D; but it has been found that after seven or eight years new breeds of pests come into existence and attack the crops anew. It is therefore necessary to keep changing to different seeds and different pesticides periodically. Biotechnology may give us some transgenic varieties. But since everything changes and adapts itself in nature, we can never rest thinking that we have found a seed variety that will be free from biotic stresses.

Present actions for a stable food security may be based on these lessons learnt from the Green Revolution that are enumerated in Report 9.

- The schemes largely concentrated on technology parameters and have been largely common across various regions of the country.
- The technological parameters across the regions vary significantly and attempts are made to adjust these into the objectives of the schemes, but this is not done at many times.

- The schemes have rarely focused on economic parameters in order to create incentives for the farmers in terms of price, marketability and market access and other infrastructure.
- A few schemes have focused on creation of employment and infrastructure. However, when the scheme is withdrawn, a sudden void in the employment as well as infrastructural sector gets created.
- Some of the schemes do not sustain the initial thrust that they created and such force gets dissipitated over the years. This thrust withers away due to the withdrawal of incentives and therefore sustainability in the growth of crops cannot be achieved.
- In terms of accrued benefits these schemes certainly helped some regions but a few regions stayed away from achieving the benefits. Therefore, regional equity in designing and implementation of the schemes is one of the most important components.
- Some of the schemes could not be continued for a longer period due to various constraints and these were merged/modified under the new schemes. In the process of transition some of the good achievements of the initial schemes were lost.

Of course, when we point out existing problems with the agriculture sector, it is not to undermine the remarkable performance that has been achieved over the past four decades. The sharp increase in numbers speak for themselves. The total production of cereals during 1960–61 was 69.0 million tonnes. During 2001–02, it rose to 198.8 million tonnes. The yield per hectare during 1960–61 was 753 kg/ha. By 2001–02 it had become 1983 kg/ha.

These achievements are due to extensive applications of agricultural research. In recent years private sector enterprises have also entered into agricultural research.

Various aspects of these developments and newer challenges from resistant pests, degraded soils, new international regulations regarding intellectual property rights pertaining to the agricultural field etc. are discussed in Report 5 of the *State of the Indian Farmer* which addresses Technology and IPR issues. Some of these, which are crucial to those who are interested in introducing newer technologies to benefit agriculture in India, are extracted here.

> Our research also shows that only a fraction of these inputs have been received under formal material transfer agreements (MTAs). In most instances techniques and material are being used without permission from patent holders. In fact, we find that Indian researchers do not have a clear idea of the extent of the proprietary technologies they use. Presently, they can use these inputs without a licence as India does not recognize patents for life forms and therefore, the patents are not valid in India. The situation will change when India changes its patent laws in accordance with TRIPs. The companies that own the technology will be able to get patents in India. When this happens, the continuation of research to develop transgenic crops in India will depend on our ability to get licences to use various proprietary techniques and material. This will make the fate of some of the important research efforts, such as Bt cotton and Bt rice projects, uncertain.

*

The public sector's weak position in agricultural biotechnology can have serious implications for India's ability to use biotechnology for poorer farmers, most of whom grow the so-called orphan crops and live in unfavourable agro-climatic regions. As these farmers are poor, they do not form a substantial seed market. Therefore, we cannot expect the private sector to develop transgenic plants of the crops which are grown by these farmers. In order to fulfil its mandate, the public sector will need to explore various alternatives to get access to biotechnology-based technologies and products. An obvious strategy will be to get access through licences to proprietary technology for use in crops grown by small and marginal farmers and suitable for harsh agro-economics climates. This may be possible for two reasons:

Firstly, the loss of a potential market by allowing the use of the technology in these crops would not involve a significant loss of market for technology owners. As the farmers who grow these crops live in harsh environments and are poor, their purchasing power is small. They do not form an important market for genetically modified

FOOD   125

plants. Therefore, by giving a licence to the public sector the technology owners will not incur a significant loss of market.

Secondly, the licensing of such technologies will provide biotechnology companies with an opportunity to improve their public image. In fact, it is also possible that in some circumstances the public sector may be permitted to use these technologies free of cost. This has already happened with the so-called 'golden rice'.

*

To summarize, there has been a large increase in the use of IPRs to protect agricultural inventions and seeds globally. As a member of the WTO, India is also required to extend IPR protection to plant varieties. It is also required to provide patent protection to life forms, including microorganisms and microbiological processes.

*

It must, however, be emphasized that private companies will focus only on those crops and traits which provide high profit margins. They are unlikely to work on crops grown by poor farmers in marginal areas. The improvement of productivity of these crops will continue to be the responsibility of the public sector research system. Similarly, small and marginal farmers do not constitute an important market for small seed companies. A strong public sector is required to address the problems faced by these farmers. This suggests that, in spite of the increased role of the private sector, the public sector will need to maintain its strength.

There are, therefore, a lot of new challenges before Indians looking to advance crops and cultivation further—not just laboratory-based research and simple extension services, but a complex network of intellectual property rights (IPRs), licensing, negotiations, public policy to cover poor and marginal farmers, financing, business management etc.

Let us now look at another major sector related to food, namely, animal husbandry.

Animal husbandry

Domesticated cattle existed in India as far back as the time of the Indus Valley civilization; even during the Aryan period animals played a major role in society. Domesticated animals were used for food; for transport; for farm work; and as companions. The waste from animals was also used as manure for food crops. Domesticated animals are also known as livestock, while birds used for flesh and eggs are called poultry.

According to Report 12 of the *State of the Indian Farmer*, the 1992 data on Indian livestock and poultry is as under. Today's figures will be higher of course.

Cattle (Cows and Oxen)	205 million
Buffaloes	84 million
Goats	115 million
Sheep	51 million
Pigs	13 million
Poultry	Over 307 million

In addition there are cart and pack animals like donkeys, camels etc.

When we finished the India Vision 2020 exercise in 1996, India was ranked second in the world in total milk output. In 2000 India became the largest milk producing country in the world with an annual output of 78 million metric tonnes. Meat production was at 4.5 million tonnes a year, with 31.5 billion eggs and 400 million broiler chickens produced a year. The production of wool, another important animal-sourced product (though not a food item) was at 6.4 million kg during 2000–01.

In 1998–99, the total output value of the livestock sector in India was about Rs 123,076 crore. Export earnings from livestock and related sectors were Rs 2,073 crores (of this leather-related items were about 54 per cent and meat about 37 per cent).

The livestock sector accounts for about 25 per cent of the total value of agriculture and allied activities in India. Among the livestock sector milk forms about 67 per cent of the value. The share of poultry and eggs is around 9 per cent, and is expected to grow further as these are a good and relatively inexpensive source of nutrition for most Indians. It is projected that by 2020, the total milk consumption in India will be around 160 million tonnes and meat around 8 million tonnes. It is interesting to note that average milk consumption by an Indian is still below the standard set by the Indian Council of Medical Research (ICMR) which is about 220 gm per capita. By 2000 India's consumption has reached 211 gm per capita.

The livestock sector is a good source of employment and income for farmers. For most of the marginal farmers it provides over 70 per cent of their supplementary income. Regular employment in this sector is for about 18.4 million people (that is about 5 per cent of the main workforce in the country). There are very little subsidies from the government for this sector but there are various insurance schemes available from public sector companies.

Livestock require plant-based food, known as feeds and fodders. In the case of goats, sheep etc. in India almost 100 per cent of their food comes from grazing on common property lands. For cattle about 33 per cent of the food comes from such sources. Such common property grazing land is estimated to be around 120 million hectares. They are heavily overgrazed, and most of them are in a state of denudation. This is both an environmental concern and a food security issue. During the initial decades of the twenty-first century new innovative solutions need to be found, keeping in mind that the owners of such cattle and small animals are nor rich and have meagre resources to spend on fodder and feed.

India also has a growing animal feed industry, the compounded total of which was about 12 million tonnes in 2001. This comprises only 25 per cent of the raw ingredients available, since not all the animal feed is up to the standards of a balanced animal diet set by the Bureau of Indian Standards (BIS). India has only about 200 large feed milling plants, with a 100 to 500 million tonnes per day (mtpd) capacity, in all; thousands of smaller ones with varying quality standards have a capacity of 8 to 50 mtpd each.

While there is a scarcity of good animal feed on the one hand, very large quantities of agricultural waste (which form a good base for animal feed) are routinely burnt as part of the waste disposal system. Millions of wheat straws in Gujarat and rice straw in Punjab and Haryana are burnt every year. Cycles of low rainfall also lead to the loss of animal feed. Unfortunately, industrial scale palletizing or briquetting of straw does not take place in India; if straw from excess years is palletized and stored it would be useful in years of scarcity.

Apart from the availability of fodder and feed, health of livestock is another key issue. The death of an animal is a great loss to the farmer, especially the marginal and poor farmer, and diseased animals lead to all kinds of complications. Thanks to veterinary services rinderpest has been eradicated from India during the mid-nineties. Other major diseases of concern are Foot and Mouth Disease (FMD) and Pests of Small Ruminants—goats etc. (PSR). Sadly, animal health care is a vastly neglected area in India.

As the country grows economically and as more people become affluent and reside in urban areas, they cannot assume that they are free from these problems which supposedly affect only the poor farmers in rural areas. As we have seen in earlier chapters, all life forms are interconnected in some way. Over the past decade you will have noticed outbreaks of many new diseases such as bird flu and swine flu. The microbes and viruses prevalent in animals also migrate to human beings and can cause disease epidemics among the human population. In addition, we also consume lots of milk and meat, which can be carriers of diseases. Animal bacteria can also enter the human body through vegetables, fruits and grains, if there is a major outbreak of disease among the animal population.

It is important therefore that the science and technology of animal and bird health care are studied and applied in India in accordance with the guidelines set by the World Trade Organization (WTO). This is important for human health care too, apart from the angles of food security and economics. The WTO mechanism will also bring in the challenge of price competition (from foreign suppliers), and Indian products will have to conform to international quality and safety standards.

The livestock sector in India has many constraints at present because very little government attention has been given to this sector on which millions of poor farmers depend. As Report 12 of the *State of the Indian Farmer* says:

> There are many constraints for improving livestock production in India: very large numbers, very poor productivity, tiny animal holdings, widely scattered production systems, shrinking land holdings, acute scarcity of feeds and fodder and recurring ravages of animal epidemics. Poor accessibility to good quality credit, government-run, centre-based veterinary and artificial insemination services and government policies based on social and religious sentiments further compound the inefficiency of the small holder livestock production systems.

*

> The most decisive role that the government can play is of designing a policy framework for the livestock sector, to redefine the role the government should play in the livestock sector and to restructure the institutional setup for livestock services delivery, within the overall development perspective for the country and in keeping with the liberalized national and global economic environment.

*

> A network of institutions responsible for trade, commerce, export, quality and safety, functioning in close coordination with each other, should be the constant watchdog to protect India's interests and to take counter-measures against arbitrary standards, procedures, codes, as well as disputes, in the WTO dispute settlement panels and forums.

It is certainly not enough to leave the sector at the mercy of market forces and investors alone or to the WTO derived standards. The science and technology required for the development of the livestock sector is easily available from foreign countries. The challenge is to adapt them to Indian sizes, which are small, and to our requirements. We must not forget that a large number of farmers are dependent upon the livestock sector and the transition to large size holdings will take a few decades more.

One of the successful Vision 2020 projects that TIFAC undertook was at Ludhiana, aimed at clean milk production with very low bacterial content. This required a system of training milk farmers right from the stages of giving cattle clean fodder, the cleaning of cattle udders before milking, cleaning of the hands of the persons engaged in milking, checking the health of the milk before milking with simple devices, mechanized milk extraction, facilities for immediate cooling etc. The TIFAC project achieved success with about fifty animals. The same methods have subsequently been applied successfully in other states.

There are about 7,750 veterinary hospitals and polyclinics in India, in addition to about 15,555 veterinary dispensaries and about 27,550 veterinary aid centres. There are also several excellent specialized animal science institutes under the Indian Council of Agricultural Institutes (ICAR), the apex agricultural research and extension services organizations in the country. Though not all of these institutions are as active as they ought to be, they have in them some excellent scientists and technologists. Here is a quick summary of their resources:

Sl.No	Institutions	Scientists	Tech Staff	Rs Lakh
1	Indian Veterinary Research Institute	294	412	1661.55
2	National Dairy Research Institute	219	418	1181.52
3	Central Sheep and Wool Research Institute	82	10	257.62
4	Central Institute for Research on Goat	38	66	70.68
5	Central Avian Research Institute	37	56	198.48
6	National Bureau of Animal Genetic Resources	12	18	36.24
7	Indian Grassland and Fodder Research Institute	109	15	159.52
8	National Research Centre for Camel	7	10	72.55
9	National Research Centre for Yak	5	-	24.73
10	National Research Centre for Equine	6	11	118.48
11	National Research Centre for Mithun	2	4	12.49
12	Central Institute for Research on Buffaloes	20	5	157.27
	Total	831	1025	3951.13

Food processing: According to Report 12, meat for domestic consumption (beef, veal, lamb, mutton, chicken and pork) is processed in some 3,643 slaughterhouses around the country. Of these, only a few, located in the metros, have the modern equipments and facilities required for hygienic processing. In the rest, there are problems in terms of the technology used and therefore in the quality. This is another area that requires urgent attention.

There are about 100,000 large and medium scale layer and broiler farms in the country. But only about 4 per cent of the total poultry meat is processed, and even here there are serious problems with the cold chain facilities. Four egg processing plants built with international collaboration exist, each of which has a capacity to process about 1 million eggs per day. These plants are technologically sophisticated.

Report 12 gives us the following information about the state of equipment and machinery manufacture.

India has a fairly well developed equipment manufacturing industry in the food and dairy sector. Almost 90 per cent of the dairy industry's requirement in machinery and equipment are made in the country itself. Imports are still required in the packaging sector, pasteurizers, heat exchangers, homogenizers and other highly sophisticated areas. For other livestock products manufacture of processing equipment is still in the early stages of development as the demand for such equipment is yet to exert pressure on the manufacturing industry. In the livestock feed milling sector all equipment for a conventional feed mill including pellet mills are made in the country. With the opening up of the economy and liberalization of procedures for foreign investments even possibility for manufacture of modern, energy-efficient equipment for the food/feed processing industry is fast becoming a possibility in India.

With the growth of the middle class with disposable incomes, and also due to pressures from international standards of cleanliness and hygiene, there are major changes in the offing for the production and processing of livestock-based food products. If slaughterhouse wastes are utilized well, the by-products from these can also provide additional income and employment. When not utilized well, they are hazards for the environment and hygiene.*

Livestock and the environment: Livestock production and the grazing land that is required for this are intrinsically linked to the environment. The human population in India has increased almost

---

*There is a full report from TIFAC on slaughterhouse wastes, which can be found on www.tifac.org.in.

five-fold in the six decades since Independence, and it is still growing. As the population grows, the demand for food (crops, vegetables, meat, poultry, fish etc.) is bound to grow too.

In earlier times, livestock in India was mostly confined to households. People kept cows, goats, pigs etc. based on the availability of fodder/feed from their own marginal farm operations and from the local areas. Mostly the livestock formed a supplementary income for their subsistence. But this age-old trend is changing fast. Households are not aiming at traditional forms of self-sufficiency any more, whether it is for feed or fodder or for the milk, meat etc. that is produced. They are now integrated into the market economy from which they draw resources and into which they contribute products. There is a gradual transition from subsistence to marketization.

Left to themselves, much of the livestock would be at a reasonable balance with nature. They would eat grasses and grains off the land, and their wastes would go to the earth, becoming manure for other plants. If they overgrazed they would have to bear the consequences of hunger and their population would be automatically controlled. Even with human beings living with livestock at a subsistence level within a locally self-sufficient system, as many Indians in villages did for centuries, an ecological balance was maintained. But the relative prosperity of a market economy puts tremendous pressure on the ecosystem, because our population density as well as the total population is very high and is growing further.

As the demand for livestock products grows, the number of cattle and other domestic animals is also growing, but due to the lack of resources and facilities, they often live in a state of neglect. Water and grazing land, which are hard to come by, have to be found for the added numbers. This puts undue pressures on the environment, leading to deforestation. On the other hand, commercial pressures for high yields and better productivity lead to the selection of only a few of the breeds for intensive breeding (this is called intensive livestock management). This again means there is a loss of biodiversity. At another level excessive animal wastes like urine, dung, dead and discarded parts of animals not only pollute water bodies but the animal emissions with their high methane content contribute to global warming as well.

A solution to these problems cannot be arrived at by trying to go back to the stage before both human and domestic animal/bird populations went up manifold. The solution lies in the judicious use of the scientific and technological knowledge within the constraints of economic systems. The modern societal demands are not only to just reduce or control the environmental damage or pollution but also to save the natural resources and enhance them.

Some of the goals are:

- Zero wastage
- Recycle and reuse
- Very low energy usage
- Recharge overdrawn water bodies
- Recreate forestry
- Reduce loss of biodiversity
- Recover as many species as possible and keep these alive in natural conditions.

Report 12 enumerates the steps that need to be taken:

Policies need to be designed to correct negative environmental effects of livestock production. These policies should address the underlying causes of environmental degradation and must be flexible, site-specific and well targeted. The main purpose of these policies is to establish the use of feedback mechanisms that ensure that the use of livestock is consistent with overall social objectives. The goal is not simply to reduce the environmental damage by reducing the polluting load, but also to enhance and save natural resources as much as feasible.

i. Use of technologies that increase efficiency of resource use: Feed is a major cost item, typically accounting for 60 to 70 per cent of the production costs. Better feed conversion saves land used for its production while reducing the animals' waste load. Some of the technologies which are most appropriate for the Indian situation are: (a) Urea molasses lick block, (b) Treatment of straw with urea, (c) Bypass protein feed, and (d) Bypass fat.

The technology in case of (a) is very simple. Urea and other supplement nutrients are mixed with molasses to make it palatable to livestock. In addition, molasses provide the energy needed in order to realize the improved microbial growth that can result from enhanced ammonia levels.

The efficiency of digestion in the rumen requires a diet that contains essential nutrients for the fermentative microorganisms. Lack of these nutrients lower animal productivity and raise methane emissions per unit of product. For low-producing animals, the primary limitation to efficient digestion is the concentration of ammonia in the rumen. Supplying ammonia can, therefore, greatly enhance digestive efficiency and utilization of available feed energy. The technology of treatment of straw with urea is based on a similar principle. Urea is broken down in the rumen to form ammonia, and adding urea to the diet has been the most effective method of boosting rumen ammonia levels.

Technologies for bypass protein and fat feeds also help greatly in resource saving and are ideally suited to the needs of high-producing animals such as cross-breeds and exotic cattle.

ii. Increase feed and fodder availability through conservation and improved moisture and nutrient supply: While the precise gap of feed and fodder between the actual demand–supply situation may still be a debatable figure, it is certain that the magnitude of the problem could worsen further in the years to come and pose a serious threat to the environment if immediate steps are not taken to rectify the situation.

The conservation agriculture approach can be promoted through integrated and synergistic management of resources. Build-up of soil organic matter and related biological activity may be boosted to optimum sustainable levels (for improved moisture and nutrient supply and soil structure) through the use of compost, farmyard manure, green manures, surface mulch, enriched fallows, agroforestry, cover crops and/or better crop residue management.

- Integrate crop and livestock production in both the cereal-based farming and agro-pastoral systems through on-farm production and conservation of fodder crops for dry seasons feeding, better use of crop residues for feed and bedding, returning manure to the land and controlled grazing is arable lands.
- Improve and increase fodder crop production on bunds and boundaries and as small fodder banks on farmers' lands.
- Production of fodder grasses, legumes and fodder trees in public and forest lands.
- Propagation of stall feeding for cross-breeds and high yielding animals.
- Promote participatory, ecology oriented, joint-forest management, in which the forest department, local people and NGOs collaborate on a holistic approach in which the livestock, fuelwood, food and livelihoods—all of the local community's needs—are linked to forest and wasteland management.

iii. Reduce grazing pressure by levying grazing fees for Gomals and other common property resources or alternatively ensure implementation of a cut and carry policy. The introduction of such policies requires institutional capabilities as well as political will to tackle the issue of fairness, with owners of larger herds paying more on a per head basis.

iv. Promote lease markets for bullocks as well as tractors so as to enable farmers to lease either of the two as per his requirement. Such markets can contribute tremendously to the environmental sustainability and viability of the draft economy.

v. Encourage campaigns and programmes which help in accelerating declining trends in the populations of desi cows and bullocks. Castration of scrub bulls and cross-breeding programmes have greatly contributed to the declining trend in the past.

vi.   Enforce regulations for the maximum BOD levels for the effluent
      discharge from leather tanning and other livestock processing
      units including dairy processing units.

Added on to these there are many more challenges due to WTO
regimes, ranging from the availability of technologies (which may
be intellectual properties of foreign countries or companies, thus
imposing additional costs for purchase) to adhering to new
standards of sanitation and hygiene in the domestic sectors in
which global companies see a market. In order to master these we
need a combination of policies that work in the interest of the
people, an understanding of market economics, and the proper
utilization of the knowledge derived from science and technology.

Fisheries

Let us now move to another important area of food production:
fisheries. This sector is dealt with extensively in Report 13 of the
State of the Indian Farmer.

Fishing has been practised for many centuries by Indians in the
coastal areas and along riversides or around lakes and ponds. Many
of the fisherfolk are poor. On the other hand, modern scientific and
technological knowledge in this area has grown by leaps and
bounds. Therefore there is a wide gap between the earnings of
fisherfolk who use traditional methods and those who use modern
techniques.

India has a long coastline of about 8,118 km. In addition to the
coastal waters, there is also a vast area of the ocean which is
available exclusively to India. The Exclusive Economic Zone (EEZ)
comprises about 2 million sq. km of which about 0.86 million sq. km
is around the east coast, 0.6 million sq. km around the Andaman
and Nicobar Islands, and the rest in other coastal areas. India has
an exclusive right to protect, conserve and utilize the benefits from
these regions.

The total harvestable marine fishery resources from these EEZs
is about 3.9 million tonnes. About 58 per cent of these are available

very near the coastline, at a 0 to 50 metre depth; about 35 per cent between 50 and 200 metres and 7 per cent beyond 200 metres. As pointed out before, most of the fishing here is still done with the aid of traditional boats or crafts. About 230,000 fishing boats are in use in the country, mostly made of wood. About 45,000 of these have a motor fitted onto the boat which helps it go faster. The productivity of these traditional craft, i.e. the fish catch per trip, is very low. Countries like Japan, Taiwan, China, Korea and Thailand in Asia, and many others globally, use modern equipments and large mechanized boats for fishing. Many of them not only catch the fish, but process the catch onboard and pack them as well. Dr Kalam visited a few such ships when he was on his presidential tour to Iceland.

India has very few such high-level commercial fishing enterprises. We currently have about 170 large fishing vessels of 21 metres overall length. About 54,000 boats are well mechanized—these are useful for better and deeper catches. But even the modernized fishing boats mostly concentrate on the shallower 0–80 metre depth zone.

While about 51 per cent of India's total fish production comes from the marine sector, about 49 per cent comes from inland water. The major sources of freshwater fish are the inland rivers and lakes. India has fourteen major rivers with a catchment area of over 20,000 sq. km each. There are forty-four minor rivers with a catchment area between 2,000 to 20,000 sq. km each, and also a large number of small rivers and streams, most of them seasonal. These different river systems have a combined length of about 29,000 km. They contain one of the richest aquatic genetic resources in the world.

Periodical flooding and other leakages from rivers create huge flood plain lakes, the majority of which are found in eastern Uttar Pradesh, northern Bihar, West Bengal, Assam and Manipur. These lakes occupy an important position in the inland fisheries of India as they are large in size and high in production potential. In addition smaller ponds and tanks add another 2.25 million ha to the inland fisheries area. Lastly, in the coastal zone there is a potential to develop fin and shell fish farming in about 1.2 million ha.

In addition to the above naturally occurring water bodies, human-made reservoirs also provide an excellent resource for developing fisheries. About 19,000 reservoirs are there in the country with an available fishery area between 2 and 3 million ha. The average fish yield of a reservoir in India is about 20 kg/ha/year. In comparison, Thailand produces 65 kg/ha/year, Russia 88 kg/ha/year and Sri Lanka 100 kg/ha/year. As in most sectors related to agriculture, India ranks very low when it comes to yield. The reasons are well known: poor fish seed stocking, inappropriate gear and craft and poor landing facilities, and the lack of a proper marketing infrastructure. In general, we as a country have not bothered about reaching the applications of modern science and technology-based support systems and processes to ordinary poor people who are large in number. Both the quality and quantity of our food products suffer as a result.

In spite of these problems, fish production in India has increased at a higher rate than food grains, eggs and many other food items. About 56 per cent of the population in India is fish eating, but the per capita fish consumption of the fish eating population is only 9 kg per annum. Fisheries contribute to about 1.4 per cent of the Indian GDP (1998–99). There is scope to increase this. There is also a good export potential. Around 1994–95, India's export of marine products reached US$1 billion; this figure can be much higher.

If we look at the history of fisheries in independent India, we can note that till 1962 fisheries stayed with traditional techniques without any mechanization, and the annual average production was below 0.8 million tonnes (mt). A slow phase of mechanization began then which went on up to 1988, with the annual production going up to 1.8 mt. Only since 1988 have we reached a fully utilized status in coastal areas with an annual production of around 2.8 mt.

But this is still much below the potential of 3.9 mt, and even now fish production in India is not fully managed on scientific lines.

Many of the problems have to do with the lack of infrastructure and inefficient management. India's active fisherfolk population during 1961–62 was about 234,000. By 1996–97 it was about 1,000,000—a five-fold increase in thirty-five years. With the presence of more active fishers, the area available per active fisher has been greatly reduced. In sea fishing there are no demarcations of territorial ownership, it is essentially open access. With the crowding of fishers there is increasing competition to get a better catch, which leads to increasing conflicts among fisherfolk. Overcrowding also leads to excessive exploitation of the available fish resources and indiscriminate fishing. There are periods in which the fish should be allowed to breed and lay eggs, and small fry allowed to grow; only mature fish should be fished in order to get better yield and to keep the life cycle going. Fishing indiscriminately causes damage to the growth cycles and leads to the overall depletion of resources. Mechanized boat based fishing, though technologically better in terms of yield, generates conflicts in a social milieu where many fisherfolk depend on fishing for subsistence, and a large number of fishers are competing in a smaller and smaller area to earn their livelihood. To better regulate the operation, state governments like Maharashtra, Gujarat, Kerala, Karnataka, Tamil Nadu and Andhra Pradesh have had to ban mechanized vessels from operating in the inshore areas (a distance of 5 to 10 km from the shore) and during the monsoon, which is the breeding season and growth period for fish.

But what is the long-term solution? The fisherfolk population will continue to increase as overall health care and life expectancy improves. But coastal and inland fishing zones are limited in size, and the quantity of sustainable potential yield of fishes is also finite. Also, increasing consumer demands for better quality and higher standards are bound to lead to a preference for the mechanized systems. The real solution is to bring down the number of fisherfolk directly dependent upon fishing for their subsistence—just as some of our marginal farmers need to be moved away from their current subsistence farming in small size lands to other jobs in the agriculture and other sectors. They may work in the fish processing sector in the coastal area, or in chains in nearby towns, or in produce marketing, or in totally different manufacturing/services sectors. The government has a big role to play in helping such large numbers of fisherfolk transition to new methods of living and earning. The new options and their benefits have to be explained to the fisherfolk and their families in a simple way and their confidence must be gained.

With a better regulated system, and with the induction of newer technologies to aid the fisherfolk, we can aim for the annual potential yield of 3.9 mt. But the jump from 2.8 mt to 3.9 mt will not be easy. Much of the scope for exploiting the additional 1.1 mt is in deep sea fishing, which requires more complex technologies and involves higher costs. The most lucrative component of deep sea fishing is tuna fishing, which yields high value in export markets. Tuna fish is migratory, and if they are not fished within India's EEZ, the same fish would be fished by others outside India's territory. Report 13 rightly points out that the high costs and technological complexity of deep sea fishing point to the need for regional cooperation. Nearby countries can join together and have common vessels, shared trained labour etc. These are the new directions of complex high technology businesses in the fisheries sector that must be considered.

While talking of fishing and the implementation of new technologies in the fishing sector, it will be interesting to note the role modern satellites can play here. According to Report 13:

Satellite imageries provide continuous data on sea surface temperature and chlorophyll covering the entire EEZ. This data has several applications, including mapping the potential fishing zones (PFZs) and fisheries forecast on a short- and long-term basis. These forecasts on an experimental basis reveal that the catch rate of pelagic fish in the PFZs is higher by about 60 per cent compared to that in the non-PFZs. However, the PFZ for coastal waters (<10 km) and demersal fish cannot be forecasted based on the remote sensing data available at present.

Inland capture fisheries: We have mentioned the rich genetic aquatic resources of our inland waters. Indian inland waters harbour the original germ plasm (i.e. the basic genetic material) of one of the richest and most diversified fish fauna in the world. There are about 930 fish species belonging to 326 genera in India, out of the total 25,000 fish species in the world.

Therefore when we look at inland fishing we must do so not only in terms of production figures and economics, but with a view to preserving, protecting and propagating this rich biodiversity. Even beneficial projects involving interconnected river systems must consider this biodiversity as an important element to be aware of. Estuarial fisheries (areas where big rivers meet the sea) are the most productive ecosystems in the world. Indian estuarial fisheries are very productive and are well above subsistence levels, with an average yield between 45 to 75 kg/ha/year.

Aquaculture: So far we have discussed naturally occurring fishes and their capture from various sources (seas, rivers, estuaries, ponds etc.). Aquaculture is the organized farming of fish under controlled conditions. While water is the main base for the fish, their growth is based on the application of various scientific and technological factors and the harvesting is done systematically, just like in any other agricultural field. India began aquaculture only during the 1980s. It has now emerged as one of the fastest growing food production activities in the country.

Fresh water aquaculture resources in India are as follows:

- 2.25 million ha of ponds and tanks
- 1.35 million ha of beels and derelict waters

- 2.09 million ha of lakes and reservoirs
- 0.12 km of irrigation canals and channels
- 2.3 million ha of paddy fields (part of which can be used for aquaculture).

Of this about 45 per cent of the ponds and lakes have been brought under aquaculture. The present level of aquaculture production is around 2.8 mt a year. The annual growth rate is about 6 per cent. Carps (three major carps form about 84 per cent of India's aquaculture production), catfish, prawns and mussels are the main products of Indian aquaculture.

India has a long way to go where scientific diversification of aquaculture is concerned. Even brackish water can be used for aquaculture. Only 0.14 million ha of brackish water bodies, mostly in the east coast, are currently under aquaculture, giving an annual production of 82,000 tonnes. Some cold water aquaculture takes place in Jammu and Kashmir and Himachal Pradesh.

While discussing the food aspects of fisheries it may also be useful to note the non-food economically remunerative aspects of fisheries. Report 13 gives us an idea about these.

Freshwater pearl culture: Production of cultured freshwater pearls through nuclei implantation in freshwater mussels has been a major achievement in recent years. This has opened new avenues for diversification of aquaculture practices, adding a new non-food aquaculture component to the produce. It also adds new dimensions to the economy through aquaculture practices.

Ornamental fish culture: There are about 106 potential ornamental fish from Kerala alone, out of which 51 freshwater species have a high potential for export. The National Bureau of Fish Genetic Resources (ICAR) during 2001 has listed 64 species endemic to the western ghats. Andaman and Lakshadweep seas are virgin grounds for some of the most beautiful marine ornamental fish.

Another incidental income from the fisheries sector has to do with fishing as a sport.

The most important aspect of cold water fish is that they provide excellent sport. Angling trout and mahseer gives ecstatic pleasure. Kashmir, Himachal Pradesh, parts of Uttar Pradesh and Uttaranchal, north Bengal, Nilgiris, Kolai Hills and the Munnar high ranges offer excellent sport opportunities for tourists and anglers. Sport fishery yields considerable revenue in Jammu and Kashmir and trout contributes to about 40 per cent of the state's revenue from fisheries.

As it develops, aquaculture must, however, be mindful of the pressures it puts on the ecosystem. As Report 13 warns us:

The population pressure has adversely affected the fragile upland ecosystem. The resource ecology, the aquatic habitat and their biodiversity are all under grave stress due to felling of forest trees and damming of rivers and streams. As a result the ecosystems such as the valley lakes in Kashmir, Kumaon, Ooty in western ghats and Manipur have reached higher tropic levels and as such cannot sustain fish species which it used to earlier.

Therefore it is imperative that we look for new economic opportunities. Report 13 outlines the possibilities, along with a note of caution.

Mariculture: Mariculture is expected to be a major activity in coastal areas in the years to come. Given the wide spectrum of cultivable species and technologies available, the long coastline and the favourable climate, mariculture is likely to generate considerable interest amongst the coastal population. At a time when we speak of over-exploitation in the near shore waters, limited access to capture fisheries and the need for diversification, mariculture can be an appropriate alternative. Technologies for a couple of species are presently available in the country and there is an urgent need for developing a package of practices for many more commercially important species (e.g. sea bass, sea bream).

Pearl culture: Technology for the culture of marine pearls and farming of the pearl oyster *Pinctada fucuta* in open sea as well as shore-based systems has been developed and standardized for commercial use.

The rate of growth in the warmer tropical waters of India is faster when compared with that in the temperate waters of Japan.

The commercial culture of edible oyster (*Crassotrea madrasensis*), green mussel (*Perna virids*), brown mussel (*Perna indica*), clams (*meritrix*) and *Andara granosa* in captivity has met with success. Spat is produced through controlled breeding and its rearing is done in cages, rafts, ropes floating/hanging in the sea. Entrepreneurship in mussel culture with interested markets is growing in coastal areas.

Holothuria scabra (sea cucumber) is being induced, bred and cultured as a major and preferred export item from India. Similarly, agar-yielding seaweed *Gracilaria edulis* with commercially viable productivity in three months by vegetative fragment culture (net/rope-culture) is a successful enterprise at several locations in coastal areas.

Sea bass and pearl spot have been successfully bred and their seed production technology has been standardized. Entrepreneurship response would determine the commercial projects with necessary institutional finance assured. These species will form viable choices for shrimp farmers as well as an alternative crop for ecological balance of the coastal aquaculture systems.

However, with a possible scenario of large-scale mariculture activities taking place in the near future, it is likely that a situation akin to shrimp farming can be created where an unplanned and fast growth has resulted in social conflicts and challenges to the sustainability of the coastal environment. To avoid repeating the shrimp story, a systematic investigation of the entire coastline would be necessary, to prepare a comprehensive status on the area-wise suitability of the available mariculture technologies, carrying capacity of the ecosystem, social, legal and environmental implications, research and policy support, credit availability and other forward and backward linkages.

Aquatic ecosystems and pollution: Pollution is the biggest problem we face when looking to sustain aquatic ecosystems. Some of the sources of pollution are listed in Report 13.

The most important types of industries which contribute to the deterioration of rivers comprise of pulp and paper, textiles, tanneries, sugar, distilleries, hydrogenated vegetable oil, coal washeries, petro-chemical and several miscellaneous products like antibiotics, chemicals, steel, dairies, fertilizers, pesticides, paints, varnish, rubber and jute etc.

The direct discharge of industrial effluents into the rivers and the run-off from fields into ponds, lakes and rivers is gradually causing serious concerns about water pollution, particularly with respect to inland fisheries. These effluents and run-offs from fields, which comprise chemicals of a versatile nature, have a highly toxic effect on the fish population by depleting the dissolved oxygen, altering the pH, the salinity, changing the carbon dioxide content and thereby directly or indirectly affecting the life cycle as well as metabolic activity of the fish at the biochemical level.

Pollution of rivers, streams and even confined water bodies with industrial and community waste is quite common. Discharge of such waste water increases the organic load (BOD) of the water, thereby decreasing the oxygen content. In such cases instances of a total loss of biotic community at the outfall region are not uncommon. But in running streams, due to the effect of dilution, planktons are expected to revive within a short distance from the outfall area. The extent of revival zone will normally depend in such cases upon the strength of pollutants and the quantity of freshwater discharge.

Large-scale deforestation in the catchment region of the river systems has posed a serious threat to the aquatic environment, especially in the upper reaches of the originating points of the rivers. Mass destruction of forest cover for timber and fire not only disturbs the delicate balance of the forest ecosystem but also leads to erosion of the topsoil bringing a high silt load in the river basin. Heavy siltation, drastic reduction in water volume, constant changes in the river course and loss of the breeding grounds of fish are some of the major factors responsible for a decline in the fisheries of major rivers such as Brahmaputra, Ganga, Yamuna and their tributaries.

Aquaculture is not a standalone activity—it interacts with the environment and uses natural resources. Since it is a live system, it constantly receives microbes from and gives microbes of various sorts to the ecosystem within which it operates. It is necessary to study these scientifically in order that they do not adversely affect themselves or create problems elsewhere.

With respect to estuarine pollution, Report 13 has this to say:

> Man-made pollution is perhaps the biggest threat to estuaries. Pollution of estuaries is difficult to assess because of the special qualities of an estuarine environment. Besides, estuarine pollution is different from river pollution, as the pollutants remain trapped in the ecosystem for a longer period due to tidal oscillations. It is also a fact that the biological resources of a typical estuary are far more important than those of a typical freshwater river in that besides prawn and fish, they also harbour oysters, snails, lobsters and a variety of water fauna.

The danger of pollution is a real threat, but this does not mean that mankind should desist from developing aquaculture and expanding fisheries. The key is to use our scientific and technological knowledge to the best effects, to minimize the risks.

> It is possible to believe that pollution is an all-pervasive deadly threat to fisheries and aquaculture, but then there are increasing arguments to emphasize that the scope of the hazards is being stretched too far. However, the scale and sophistication of industrial pollution has become alarming in certain parts of the world, including India. Setting technical standards for the control of such pollution is bound to be debatable. In the absence of certainty regarding cause and effect, we must assume that the most reasonably suspected effects actually do occur and formulate our policies according to the so-called highest reasonable risks. This could facilitate consideration of all possible strategies for pollution control.

There are several other value-added activities related to the fisheries sector. The fish processing industry provides employment to a large number of people. Several by-products, like the chemical glucosamine hydrochloride which is derived from fish shells and is useful in geriatric care to relieve joint pain, are also part of the benefits of fisheries. Report 13 lists some of the important processed fish products and by-products.

Indian export of fish and fish products consists not only of the whole fish but a large number of processed products having direct entry into retail markets of American and European countries with Indian brand names. The highly valuable products are frozen fish and shellfish, live fish, lobsters and crabs, filleted fish products, canned fish and shellfish, ready-to-serve curry in flexible pouches with very long shelf life, cured fish, rack dried fish, IQF fish products, dehydrated jelly fish, beche-de-mer (sea cucumber), masmin/masmin flakes (from tuna), fish wafers/soup powder, battered and breaded value-added products, pickles etc.

There are a number of by-products obtained from fish and shellfish (prawn and shrimp) during the course of their processing. These products have important applications in medicine, surgery, industry and food processing. They are chitin and chitosan, fish feed, surgical sutures from freshwater carp guts, collagen-chitin film (used as artificial skin), shark cartilage, squalene from shark liver oil, shark fin rays, isinglass for the liquor industry, concentrated PUFA from fish oil with Omega3 fatty acids, agar-agar and agarose from seaweed, insulin, fish albumin, glucosamine hydrochloride, bile extracts, drugs/chemicals from seaweed, and steroids and other compounds from marine animals.

∼

We have made a sweeping survey of various food sources. The role of modern science, technology and management methods is to help in the transition from subsistence food agriculture, so that the yield is increased and abundant food is available, and so that people engaged in food-related services work more systematically and earn more. More scientific techniques have to be employed and people taken away from direct subsistence levels and deployed in other value-adding activities. This requires a great deal of community engagement, learning and training. And all through, care for ecosystems and biodiversity would need special understanding. We should also know that India is a party to various international agreements and organizations like WTO which bring in several constraints as well as opportunities. These also require scientific understanding and its percolation from the policy level to the people level.

India has the potential to do all this, provided we dedicate ourselves to the task, and do not lose time.

In many of his talks on food, Dr Kalam has quoted the example of the increase in yield in Bihar achieved as part of the TIFAC Vision 2020 agriculture project to show how agriculture can progress from the subsistence level to much higher levels using the right application of scientific and technical knowledge. He has also referred often to the Clean Milk Vision 2020 project of TIFAC, and has also laid emphasis on agro-food processing. An address on 25 September 2003, delivered at the inauguration of the Food Processing Park at Kakkanchery in Kerala encapsulates his main thoughts and suggestions on the subject.

———————————

I find that the KINFRA Food Park at Malappuram has a tie-up with United Nations Industrial Development Organization to assist the units in training and research. The entrepreneurs would get UNIDO approved processing technology and training in coconut products and others. The park has the potential to become a very good export unit and I am sure the local farmers and the entrepreneurs will benefit from this venture.

The unit presently appears to have fifteen allottees and three of them have started production in the site. The main product coming out of this park is vegetable oil and it has a good turnover of Rs 75 crores. However, I find the palmolin required for refining is coming from other countries. This situation has to change. Our farmers have to be educated to take up the cultivation of palmolin in the local farms and the high yield variety palmolin must be processed by this unit which will be beneficial both to the farmers and the entrepreneurs. This type of value addition is what we are looking for from our entrepreneurs. They can even resort to contract farming on the lines of Punjab with support from the state government. The other two units which have been started are catering to the needs of packaging elements required by the oil industry and the ice cream unit. The turnover from these units requires enhancement.

Infrastructure and connectivity

The establishment of this park at a cost of Rs 19.5 crore and with the infrastructure such as water, power, drainage system and roads has definitely enhanced the economic activity in the region. Now is the time we should increase the economic activity by creating more units in the park for which the technology can be drawn from the Defence Food Research Laboratory and the Central Food Technology Research Institute of Mysore. These institutions have been working in the area of food processing and food preservation for three to four decades. They have infrastructure and facilities required for preservation, storage, testing and quantity production required by the armed forces and the trade. The park can have periodic meetings with the local entrepreneurs and arrange networking of these institutes for determining the products which can have a viable off-take for the local and the export market.

Kerala has a number of people living in the Gulf and the Middle-East region. They are very keen to have homely food which the park can manufacture, export and provide in a ready-to-eat form. Some of the products which have already been developed and the technologies available for transfer are halwa, upma, rava idli, pulav, khichdi, bisse-bele bhath, avial, potato peas curry, mutton and vegetable soups, omelettes, scrambled eggs etc. Production of these items in the park will automatically give the farmers in the region a ready market and remunerative prices for their agricultural output. Our agricultural universities can work with food processing units and provide them technology and knowhow for these products.

Fish processing and opportunities

I would like to share with you the experience of the fishing industry in a seafaring country. There a ship goes to the sea and catches a lot of fish and stores it in the deck. The fish are then transferred to another ship. The entire process of washing, cleaning, cutting and addition of preservatives preparing it as food are done in the processing lab. A third ship comes and collects the entire packaged value-added goods from the second ship for transporting into the international market.

I would visualize a similar situation in this Food Processing Park in the form of agricultural produce coming into the park, getting processed, value added and packaged and delivered to the second set of vehicles for conveyance to the market.

Coconut, vegetables and fruits processing

Kerala is rich in coconut, fish, plantains, cashew nuts and jackfruit. All these items can be converted into cashable products. For example, if we take coconut, all parts of the coconut tree are useful as a household product. The leaves are used for thatched roof, its stem can be used for producing broomsticks, the trunk of the tree can be used as beams, coconut water can be used as a beverage, coconut in different forms can be used for preparing chutneys, additives to curries, and copra for producing oil. The entire economics of the coconut if judiciously used can give us multifold benefits. This has to be done by the food processing unit through large cooperatives so that coconut growers get sufficient revenue.

Similar projects can be undertaken for utilizing the other agricultural products like fruits, vegetables, milk and poultry produced in Kerala.

The core technologies needed for such processing would involve cold chains, packaging, processing, aseptic packing and weighing and sensing equipment. Such facilities must be established by the infrastructural development corporation and given on hire to different entrepreneurs.

In the India 2020 document, the vision of transforming India into a developed nation has been projected. It involves the integrated development of agriculture and food processing, education and health care, information and communication technology, infrastructure and self-reliance in critical technologies. Agriculture and food processing are the most important areas for development relating to this park. Seventy per cent of the population of the country is working in the area of agriculture. Even though they produce 200 million tonnes of products, the farmer is not getting adequate remuneration for the efforts he puts in. Food items produced in such parts require value addition through technology. Particularly, I would like the food processing industry in Kerala to set a modern trend in quality, ensure availability of the product at the right time and at the right price. Every product coming out of this centre should have a label of what it contains, what are the additives, what preservative material has been used, what is the shelf life and also an assurance certifying the quality of the product. With this approach, Kerala food processing units can become globally competitive. KINFRA can also support a programme for making a mobile agro-processing unit which can travel in the whole region. With this model, entrepreneurs can establish small-scale food processing industries in the region depending upon local needs and resources.

Chapter 8

ENERGY, ELECTRICITY, WATER

In the previous chapter, we looked at one of the resources that is the very basis for human survival, i.e. food. In this chapter, we will discuss the other vital elements that are crucial both for survival and civilization, namely energy and water.

Human beings started out as food gatherers, drawing on nature for their sustenance. Later, the discovery of fire allowed them to cook food, and also to forge better weapons out of metals; thus they became hunters. Subsequent inventions such as the wheel allowed Man to access and use energy, and thus began his climb up the civilizational ladder.

A great new beginning was made with the advent of the agricultural era about 10,000 years ago. The use of energy and water now took many different forms: dams, canals and wells were built, and animal power was used for transportation as well as cultivation. Various building materials were designed through the use of fire and housing projects began in full earnest. The use of water increased as the ability to store water for agricultural and community use evolved. Soon the use of energy and water became an index of civilization.

During the industrial revolution in the nineteenth century, internal combustion engines took the use of energy and water to much greater and more efficient levels. Steam engines that used coal as fuel and petroleum-based engines revolutionized manufacturing, transport and even agriculture. With the large-scale use of electric power, civilization attained modernity. Today, we cannot imagine doing without electricity; it is a part of our life at every step. But even now about 600 million Indians do not have access to electricity. This is one of the main reasons that we are not able to reach many new knowledge benefits, skills or technological opportunities to them. Even EDUSAT cannot reach educational content to a place where there is no electricity and reception is not possible. Modern electric tools and machines, including medical equipment, cannot be used there.

With the easy availability of energy and electricity, living standards go up. With the enhancement of living standards, consumption levels of several consumer goods, especially clean water, go up as well, as the perceptions regarding the maintenance of health and hygiene become accentuated. The production of purified water involves the expenditure of power, and puts pressures on the finite supply of water that is at our disposal on the planet.

It is easy to see how, in modern civilization, energy, electricity and power are always closely linked. We would like to have at least a minimum availability of these three things for all Indians. Today India ranks very low in per capita consumption of these items; our rank is above 100, whereas given the size of our country, our resources and our population, we should be in the top 20. This can only be achieved by efficient use of our resources and by stopping wastage. For water, reduction, reuse and recycle should be our aim. In the case of energy it would be reduction, reuse and use of renewable energy. For electricity, efficiency and clean generation should be the priorities.

Let us explore some aspects of these three vital items and understand their scientific possibilities and constraints.

Energy

The only source of energy on Earth is the Sun. You may ask whether the Earth does not have other forms of energy like coal or petroleum and the renewable energy of forests, waterfalls and oceans. True, these are there. But originally the Earth itself was spun off from the Sun. So the heat inside the Earth and the source for earth fuels comes from the Sun. Life on Earth is sustained by solar energy which leads to various photochemical activities and results in the growth of plants, herbivorous animals and carnivorous ones. Even when we use manual energy or animal power, its basic source can again be traced to solar energy, even though the Sun is about 150 million km away from us.

Solar energy comes from nuclear fusion.

Let us look at the basic element hydrogen to understand nuclear fusion. A hydrogen atom has a proton in its nucleus and an electron in orbit around it. In a very hot situation like on the Sun, when all the atoms and molecules are highly agitated and moving around, they will naturally collide amongst themselves. Their high density creates a gravitational pull to make them come closer. In the process of collision, protons (which carry positive charge) and electrons (which carry negative charge) can combine to form a neutron (a neutral particle). But still many of these protons, electrons and neutrons would keep on colliding. A few of these can combine two protons and two neutrons together to make a helium nucleus. This nucleus with two positive charges can attract two electrons and form a helium atom. This is the way in which lower elements keep combining to form higher elements, going up to elements as heavy as Uranium238.

Now let us look at the helium nucleus formed by the collision. If we weigh it for mass it will not weigh exactly the same as the mass of two protons and two neutrons; the total mass will be about 0.7 per cent less. Where does the missing mass go? It is converted into thermonuclear energy. The small missing mass multiplied by c^2 (where c is the velocity of light in the vacuum) exactly accounts for the thermonuclear fusion energy. (This follows the famous $e=mc^2$ law discovered by Einstein.) Similarly if a big nucleus like that of uranium splits into lower weight elements and you add the weights of the resulting neutrons and protons of their nuclei, they don't tally exactly; a small mass will be missing, which will have converted into thermonuclear energy again, following the $e=mc^2$ law.

The first process, of joining atoms, is known as fusion, while the second process, of splitting atoms, is called fission. The entire science of nuclear power (be it to generate electric power or to power a nuclear bomb) comes from this simple principle.

The entire energy of the Sun comes from thermonuclear fusion.

The direct conversion of the small (lost) mass into energy is an extremely energy efficient process. When we burn wood or coal by raising their temperature, the molecules get excited, and new molecules get formed by combining with the oxygen in the air; as a result, energy gets generated as fire or heat. But this is a very inefficient process as only the molecules and the rotating electrons are involved, the nucleus doesn't change at all.

Nuclear fusion produces about 10 million times the energy produced by the chemical burning of an equal amount of coal. But only a very small percentage (0.7 per cent) of the protons and neutrons are converted into energy in nuclear fusion. To light a 50 watt bulb for just one second, a million atomic fusions would be required.

This may seem like an inordinately large number, but the fact is that on the Sun 2 trillion trillion trillion (10^{36}) hydrogen atoms are fused every second! So the resulting flow of energy from the Sun is about 200 trillion kilowatts in the form of sunshine on Earth.

Are you worried that the Sun with this frantic pace of fusion will burn itself out? In fact, the Sun's hydrogen availability is such that it can last for 100 billion years if it keeps burning at this pace. Due to a variety of other reasons the Sun may not live more than 10 billion years in its current form. But till now, in 4.5 billion years, it has burnt or fused only 4 per cent of its hydrogen.

It is clear that thermonuclear fusion of hydrogen is one of the most efficient sources of energy. This is why on Earth we are looking to create not only solar energy based systems but also energy systems that draw on thermonuclear fusion.

Solar energy is converted into different forms on Earth. Let us look at the various forms of energy available to human beings.

Physical energy: Our physical energy comes from the food we eat. Even now many Indians earn their income from the manual work that they do.

Animal energy: This involves the use of oxen, bullocks, horses, donkeys etc. to supplement and enhance human capabilities. Animal energy has sustained human beings from about 10,000 years ago. Even now in many parts of the world including India, people use animal power for many arduous tasks—transportation, carrying loads, drawing water, ploughing fields, crushing oilseeds to extract oil etc. With advances in technology and the advent of economic and efficient solutions for the above tasks, the use of manual labour and animal power has reduced greatly. But still many men and women will be found carrying and transporting heavy loads in India. If we have to be considered a developed nation, we need to totally abolish human energy being used to accomplish manual tasks for others.

Similarly in a developed country the use of animal power for normal economic activities will go down tremendously. One may have an occasional horse or elephant or camel ride for entertainment, but animals being used for essential economic activities will become rarer and rarer. This is not only to prevent the exploitation of animals. The use of animal energy is inefficient, in that one has to spend more resources (food and water) on an animal to get an equivalent amount of work out of it. The introduction of higher technology enables us to have a more efficient use of energy. But whether we would need to bring back animal power in some areas for reasons other than efficiency, such as the protection of biodiversity, is a matter that needs deep thought.

Fire: Dr Kalam has named the powerful missile of the Integrated Missile Development Programme, Agni. Agni, fire, is a great symbol of energy. Fire occurs naturally on Earth in the form of forest fires, volcanoes, burning of gases coming from the Earth's crust or the burning of methane which comes from decayed organic matter. But the way fire is used, both in the ancient times and even now in many parts of India, is not very efficient.

In the language of science and engineering efficiency has a precise meaning. It measures the input required for a given output. In nature nothing can be hundred per cent efficient. When you do a work, however efficiently, some energy is bound to be lost; this is measured as 'entropy'. (This is indicated by the Second Law of Thermodynamics.)

For instance, when you use an air conditioner to cool you room, the amount of disorder in the movement of molecules in the air and other bodies in the room is temporarily reduced. This is called reduction in the local entropy. But it comes at a price! Not all the energy is used in cooling the room or reducing the disorder there. A great deal of energy is converted into heat and sound by the air conditioner.

Scientists and engineers today are trying their best to build systems that utilize as much energy as possible. Cars are more fuel-efficient than before. Fans are practically sound-free so that the waste of energy as unwanted noise is reduced to a minimum. Most factories reuse the waste thermal energy by capturing it for other heating needs. There are energy audits carried out to find methods of reducing leakages of energy.

If you look at many air-conditioned rooms the doors or windows are not sealed properly. Some of the cooled air escapes as a result and hot air gets in and has to be cooled all over again. This is an unnecessary waste of energy. Similarly in many households the pressure cooker has several leakages because the rubber washer is damaged; as a result the steam escapes, wasting the heat. There are people who take out food straight from the refrigerator and heat it. We know that if you keep the food at room temperature for some time, it gets warmer on its own; as a result, your burning fuel requirement will go down since the heating is to be done only from a higher temperature.

Coming back to fire energy, early human beings used firewood very inefficiently. If the wood burning *chulha* is designed with modern scientific principles, it can not only be made smokeless but also be made firewood efficient. But there are limits to such efficiency. We need different forms of energy to make burning more efficient.

Since the modern requirements of consumption are very high and for very different and varied needs, fire and heating energy fuels must be used very efficiently so that we can enjoy more benefits with less consumption of actual energy. There are now many such devices built on scientific principles.

Coal: Earlier in this book we have discussed how coal is formed in the earth and the methods of mining it. Coal is used for burning, which converts its energy into fire and heat. Unlike wood which is loosely packed with cellulosic and other materials, coal is highly compacted carbon and therefore its energy content is much higher. Energy from coal helped humans to usher in the industrial revolution.

Naturally occurring coal is not all good compacted carbon. As it is found in the earth, it carries many other particles and materials. Most coal has some ash content as well. The quality of coal varies from mine to mine. On the whole, Indian coal contains more ash than the coal mined in some other countries like Australia. But nowadays the technology is available to remove many of these extraneous matters from coal. This is good from the point of view of the user as equipment using cleaned-up coal is much safer and more efficient. From the environmental point of view as well, emissions can be better controlled.

The best way as of now to use coal is to make it into a gas which can be burnt just like natural gas. This method is called integrated coal gasification system. When he was the principal scientific adviser to the Government of India from 1999 to 2001, Dr Kalam promoted this idea and offered to fund the development of a big prototype system. Unfortunately, the project never moved ahead.

There are now a few other technologies available to convert the energy of coal into modern useable forms such as liquid fuel and electricity. The government has recently approved a few projects in the private sector that will use such technologies, and has dedicated a few coal mines for them.

Many climate change activists would like to do away with the use of coal completely as a source to be converted into energy. This is because of its high 'carbon footprint'; when coal is burnt, the carbon in it combines with oxygen to release energy, and therefore carbon dioxide (CO_2) is produced.

The entire developed world used carbon and petroleum so inefficiently in the previous centuries that the Earth is now engulfed by the resultant polluting emissions, not just carbon dioxide but other harmful pollutants such as oxides of sulphur and nitrogen as well. Of course, they are now capable of going to much cleaner technologies derived from solar energy, higher order biofuel, hydrogen etc. But these are costly to develop and procure and also require a high investment.

To solve the global problem of pollution, developed countries would like to see densely populated developing countries like India and China adopting these technologies immediately. But the intellectual property rights (IPRs) of these technologies are held by the developed countries. IPRs come in various forms like patents, designs and trademarks. Nowadays IPRs have emerged as big business with many scientific, technical and legal experts working together.

In a way due to the IPR regime operating worldwide through the agreements resulting from the World Trade Organization (WTO)—to which India is a party—scientific ideas are no longer free and usable by all. If we want to use a new invention we have to find out who has the IPRs and negotiate with them. The licence fees might be so high that your business cannot afford them. This is an important commercial fact that all of us have to remember. It is no longer enough to develop technologies on one's own—in fact often it is not possible, since the legal rights to a specific knowledge set is held by someone else.

Today, while science and technologies open many new avenues of possibility, commercial considerations and geopolitics place various constraints on their free flow. Therefore, our science and technology policies need to be focused towards these new realities so that all Indian people can derive benefits from them. It is no longer an issue that can be left to individual scientists or institutions to decide.

To get an idea of the implications of IPRs on India, about three-fourths of the IPRs in the emerging renewable energy sector are held by US companies or institutions or individuals. Similarly in advanced areas of third generation biofuels which have very low carbon footprints (such as fuel extracted from blue green algae), the IPRs are held by the USA, a few European countries and Japan.

Though climate change lobbies are against the use of coal, India has to depend on coal for much of its electric power generation and for many factories. However, we cannot use the older technologies which pollute the atmosphere. Fly ash, a by-product of coal, affects the environment in a major way. When Dr Kalam and Y.S. Rajan were heading TIFAC, a major national fly ash utilization mission was executed. India now uses fly ash in a major way as a component of bricks and cement, which reduces the overall carbon footprint of brick and cement production. Many modern 'green' buildings which use very little energy in producing construction materials use fly ash, which is readily available.

India should work aggressively on converting coal to liquid for power and similar new technologies, since the country has an abundant supply of coal. But as far as possible, if alternate techno-economically viable energy solutions are available, coal use can be reduced in the overall interest since it contributes to global warming.

Water (hydel power): Water is not a fuel for energy in the usual sense; its energy is not released by a combustion process. Flowing water carries with it a lot of kinetic energy i.e. energy that comes from motion: it is proportional to the mass of the moving material and the square of its velocity, $\frac{1}{2} mv^2$.

Where does water get its kinetic energy from? The rain clouds which are at a height of 1 km or more above the Earth pour down rain when cooled. When the water is up in the clouds it has a large potential energy that can be measured as mgh (mass of the material x gravity x height). The higher the water is, the greater its potential energy. This potential energy is converted to kinetic energy when the water reaches the Earth.

Since most rivers begin in the mountains and are filled by rainwater or by water from glacial melts, they gush down to the plains with great force. This kinetic energy is converted into hydroelectric power. But for controlled power generation we cannot depend only on naturally flowing water. So huge dams are built to store large volumes of water and then release it, converting the kinetic energy of the flow into electricity. Dams are a complex civil engineering challenge, since the stored water exerts enormous pressure on the soil and rocks in the area. One also has to be cognizant of human populations that may be displaced and ecosystems that might be disrupted by massive hydel projects.

Hydel power projects use the kinetic energy of water to turn a turbine, which in turn, due to the dynamo effect, produces electricity. There is another way of using water energy to produce electric power. If a magnet is rotated with reasonable speed at the centre of a coil of copper wire, electricity is generated. The rotation of the magnet can be done by the water turbine. The continuous rotation of the magnet makes electricity flow in a continuous cycle of alternating current; this effect was discovered by Faraday.

Using this principle very small (micro hydel) and small (mini hydel) hydel stations can be built. Without seriously disturbing the river or canal flow, the kinetic energy from the flow can be extracted by micro or mini turbines. These are small power stations which can produce power ranging from 10 kilowatts to a few hundreds kilowatts. The great advantage of micro and mini hydel stations is that they can be used in difficult terrains and in remote areas. But the constraint is that the power from these stations is totally dependant on water flow. During summer, when the streams run dry, the availability of power is greatly reduced. If micro and mini hydel stations are to become popular they need to be operated in conjunction with another power source, operating on solar power or biofuel.

There can also be a system where micro and mini hydel stations are connected to a regional grid that carries electric power from various stations. When availability is ample, electric power from the micro and mini stations will not only feed the local residences but can also be supplied to other areas through the grid. When their power production is low the people around the micro and mini stations will get their power from outside fed through the grid.

New technologies of networking the various electric power stations through common grids and controlling the flow of electricity through electronic controls provide solutions for the future. As these high technology items become cheaper, they can help provide electricity to ordinary people who cannot pay a high price for electricity.

From the environmental point of view hydroelectric energy is clean. There is a very small carbon footprint in its operation. It is a renewable energy, but dependent on seasonal changes. This is why during summer all power grids (that draw on hydroelectricity) have to reduce supply, resulting in power cuts.

Petroleum and natural gas: This unique form of energy fuel that is found below the surface of the Earth revolutionized the twentieth century. To a very great extent, petroleum sped up the globalization process by providing fast and economic modes of transportation to human beings. It also made the large-scale movement of food grains, vegetables, machines, equipment, raw materials and finished products possible, giving rise to the consumerist culture.

In addition to being an energy source, petroleum provides the base for the wonder material called plastic, which is derived from petroleum crude. Petroleum crude is also the source for modern agricultural fertilizers that have ensured food security for the growing human population.

Not all countries are endowed with plentiful reserves of petroleum. Those that do have rich resources have prospered because petroleum is the most valued commodity in the modern world. The science and technology involving the uses, extraction and refining of petroleum have grown continuously through research. India has several big companies that concentrate on petroleum and gas extraction and refining.

The energy of petroleum and natural gas is extracted for the transportation sector to be used in the internal combustion engine, where the oil is not just burnt but mixed with oxygen in a complex manner to extract the greatest amount of energy in the most efficient manner. Early car engines were not very efficient and lots of waste gases polluted the air. But the progress of science and technology have led to clean engines with very low emissions. There are now tough standards for emissions which can be met without very heavy costs to the end consumer. Fuel-efficient cars give enhanced mileage and also emit a lesser amount of polluting materials like sulphur oxide, nitrous oxides, benzene etc.

Since petroleum and natural gas are finite resources, there are researches underway to replace them with other energy sources for transportation. There is an ongoing effort to develop cars that can run on electricity or hydrogen-based fuel. To a limited extent biofuels can also replace petroleum as an additive of 10 to 20 per cent. The new hybrid engines use part petroleum or diesel and part electric power or even solar power.

Even for electricity generation petroleum and natural gas offer an excellent option. For thermal power generation petroleum and natural gas are alternatives to coal. They cause less pollution, but their overall carbon footprint is not low enough, and so their use needs to be reduced.

Nuclear power: When it comes to environmental cleanliness, nuclear energy has a definite lead over other fuels. In the early years, nuclear power was not competitive in terms of economics; coal- and petroleum-based thermal power stations were a lot cheaper in terms of initial investment or operations. But now with the increased economic growth of many countries, the demand for petroleum, gas and coal have gone up tremendously, and the price of oil has shot up too. At the same time, nuclear power generation technologies, safety technologies and nuclear solid waste management technologies have advanced tremendously over the past three decades. Along with the current climate change concerns, nuclear power has found a new respectability. Dr Kalam has been and is a strong advocate of electricity being generated from nuclear power for civilian use.

Nuclear power stations work through fission, i.e. a big nucleus like uranium is split into smaller parts through the bombardment of neutrons. As we have seen before, the sum of the masses of the split elements is slightly less than the mass of the original uranium nucleus. The 'missing' mass gets converted to energy according to the $e=mc^2$ law. The energy released is in the form of enormous heat that is converted to electricity.

Now it is not enough to split one or a few uranium nuclei. They have to be split continuously to keep the process going. In order to do that you need a continuous supply of energetic neutrons bombarding many nuclei; there has to be a net surplus of neutrons after splitting, recombining, getting lost in some other directions etc. In other words, the chain reaction has to keep going at a particular rate. If it goes too fast, the chain reaction goes out of control and there will be an explosion (this is what happens in a nuclear bomb). If it is too slow, then after some fission and power release, the process will come to a halt, and the power plant will not be able to supply electricity.

The whole science and technology of a nuclear electricity power plant is designed to arrive at the right balance to keep the power plant going. As reactions take place at a nuclear level, the uranium available can keep going for several years. The split (non-fissionable) uranium material is collected as nuclear solid waste. This can be enriched later and reused as fuel.

Due to the limited availability of uranium, India's long-term goal is to use thorium, which is abundant in India, for nuclear power generation. But this presents a considerable scientific and technical challenge. When thorium is used in a nuclear plant, many intermediate products get formed, blocking the smooth progress of the chain reaction, making it difficult for the power plant to operate. Scientists and nuclear engineers are at work, trying to devise ways to remove the intermediate products. Once this is done, thorium will become a rich resource. Dr Kalam is a great supporter of the use of thorium because it is available in plenty in India and can greatly reduce the dependence of India on other countries for energy fuel.

Geothermal power: This involves accessing the hot materials from below the surface of the Earth and using their heat energy for power generation. Newly formed earth surfaces like Iceland have this power in abundance. In India it is limited. But it is an area where there is scope for active research and development.

Ocean tidal power: This operates on the same principle as hydroelectric power. Here the energies of the ocean waves are used to generate electricity. India has done pilot experiments in this area on the Kerala and Tamil Nadu coasts. There are concerns about the effects of power generation outfits on coastal ecology and the living resources in the ocean, which must be taken into consideration.

Wind power: The basic science here is similar to hydroelectric power generation. The wind energy is used to rotate a coil around a magnetic core—this generates electricity. The technological challenge is to make the blades of the fan as light as possible so that the wind energy can be efficiently used to move it fast. In addition to being light the blades have to be strong so that they don't break in strong winds. Fans to generate wind power are now made of the wonder material of advanced composites, which were first used in aircraft and launch vehicles. Dr Kalam was once head of the Fibre Reinforced Plastic Division (FPRD) at Thiruvananthapuram; at TIFAC too there was a major advanced composites mission. There are many uses of composite material ranging from aircraft and cars to furniture, roofs and disability aids.

Where does composite material get its strength from? To create a composite, several thin strands of strong material are fused together at high pressure and temperature. The science behind composites is simple: while conventional materials like steel are strong in all directions, the strength in composites is built up in the desired direction only, with less material. So it becomes possible to have a stronger as well as lighter material.

The one major disadvantage of wind power is that winds are not available round the clock. Therefore, it is used most often to feed an electric grid which can use wind power when it is available and switch to other forms of power at other times. As a standalone operation, wind power can be used in large agricultural fields to pump out water from the ground or from a stored place to irrigate the fields.

Solar power: Just above the Earth's atmosphere, the power of the Sun's radiation is about 1400 watts per square metre. But it is not easy to access the solar power at such a height. At the ground level, assuming various losses in the atmosphere due to scattering and reflection and also absorption by various gases present in the atmosphere, we get solar power of about 1000 watts per square metre on an average, when the sun is shining brightly. We have about 8–10 hours of good sunlight per day. That is a lot of energy that is waiting to be used.

Unfortunately, let alone capture all of this energy, we are not able to convert even 50 per cent efficiently. Those of you who live in hot places like Delhi will have noticed that in summer the water in the plastic storage tanks on the terrace is heated by the sun. But if you calculate the efficiency—the amount of sunlight that has to work on the water to heat it to a degree—it will be very low, around 1 per cent or so. Properly designed solar heaters are now available commercially; even with these the efficiency is only around 5 per cent. Of course, there are more complex designs that have optical lens and mirror systems to concentrate the solar power to specific points and pick off its energy from there, but these are very costly. To be useful for daily use, the costs of installation and operations have to be low.

We have to find inexpensive and efficient ways of obtaining solar electric power. Space satellites use solar power because other options are not available, and would be costly in terms of weight. In remote areas that have abundant sunlight and where the transport of fuel is difficult, standalone solar power systems with backup storage batteries are a good option. Such power systems use direct converters of solar power to electricity called photovoltaic materials. There are some materials like silicon that efficiently convert solar light into electricity; compounds like cadmium sulphide are also good photovoltaic materials.

Proponents of solar power project it as the power source of the future, and claim that there are no carbon emissions whatsoever from solar electricity. This is not entirely true. While there are indeed no emissions after installation, to make a solar cell and all its back-up material, a lot of energy is spent whose carbon emissions have to be taken into account. Current technologies are such that we need to spend lots of other forms of electricity to produce solar cells. Nowadays scientists and engineers have started mapping the carbon footprints of most of the materials we use right from the production to use to final disposal. This helps focus on items which are truly low in carbon generation. Titanium dioxide (titanium is available in plenty in India) is one such material.

Hydrogen power: We have mentioned that hydrogen is the primary source of the energy of the Sun, which is produced through the process of nuclear fusion. There are endeavours to create power from hydrogen the world over, including in India. But operational success is yet to be met for large-scale applications. There are a great many scientific and technological challenges involved. If you are curious you can find out more from the Institute of Plasma Research located in Ahmedabad.

Dr Kalam is passionate about India becoming 'energy independent', i.e. able to meet all its energy requirements from its own resources. This may not be realizable in the near future, but an attempt to find innovative solutions to reach electricity and other energy sources to all Indians is a crucial national challenge.

Here is an excerpt from Dr Kalam's famous presidential speech delivered on 14 August 2005.

Energy independence

Today on this 59th Independence Day, I would like to discuss with all of you another important area that is 'energy security' as a transition to total 'energy independence'. Energy is the lifeline of modern societies. But today, India has 17 per cent of the world's population, and just 0.8 per cent of the world's known oil and natural gas resources. We might expand the use of our coal reserves for some time and that too at a cost and with environmental challenges. The climate of the globe as a whole is changing. Our water resources are also diminishing at a faster rate. As it is said, energy and water demand will soon surely be a defining characteristic of our people's lives in the twenty-first century.

Energy security rests on two principles. The first, to use the least amount of energy to provide services and cut down energy losses. The second, to secure access to all sources of energy including coal, oil and gas supplies worldwide, till the end of the fossil fuel era which is fast approaching. Simultaneously we should access technologies to provide a diverse supply of reliable, affordable and environmentally sustainable energy.

As you know, our annual requirement of oil is 114 million tonnes. A significant part of this is consumed in the transportation sector. We produce only about 25 per cent of our total requirement. The presently known resources and future exploration of oil and gas may give mixed results. The import cost today of oil and natural gas is over Rs 120,000 crore. Oil and gas prices are escalating; the barrel cost of oil has doubled within a year. This situation has to be combated. Energy security, which means ensuring that our country can supply lifeline energy to all its citizens, at affordable costs at all times, is thus a very important and significant need and is an essential step forward. But it must be considered as a transition strategy, to enable us to achieve our real goal, that is energy independence or an economy which will function well with total freedom from oil, gas or coal imports. Is it possible?

Energy independence has to be our nation's first and highest priority. We must be determined to achieve this within the next twenty-five years, i.e. by the year 2030. This one major, twenty-five-year national mission must be formulated, funds guaranteed, and the leadership entrusted without delay as public–private partnerships to our younger generation, now in their thirties, as their lifetime mission in a renewed drive for nation-building.

Goals and policies

I would now like to discuss with you some goals, strategies and policies for a major national mission to attain energy independence.

Energy consumption pattern in India in 2005: We have to critically look at the need for energy independence in different ways in its two major sectors: electric power generation and transportation. At present, we have an installed capacity of about 120,000 MW of electricity, which is 3 per cent of the world capacity. We also depend on oil to the extent of 114 million tonnes every year, 75 per cent of which is imported, and used almost entirely in the transportation sector. Forecasts of our energy requirements by 2030, when our population may touch 1.4 billion, indicate that demand from the power sector will increase from the existing 120,000 MW to about 400,000 MW. This assumes an energy growth rate of 5 per cent per annum.

Electric power generation sector: Electric power generation in India now accesses four basic energy sources: fossil fuels such as oil, natural gas and coal; hydroelectricity; nuclear power; and renewable energy sources such as biofuels, solar, biomass, wind and oceans. Fortunately for us, 89 per cent of the energy used for power generation today is indigeneous, from coal (56 per cent), hydroelectricity (25 per cent), nuclear power (3 per cent) and renewable energy (5 per cent). The solar energy segment contributes just 0.2 per cent of our energy production.

Energy independence in electric power generation

Thus it would be seen that only 11 per cent of electric power generation is dependent on oil and natural gas, which is mostly imported at enormous cost. Only 1 per cent of oil (about 2–3 million tonnes of oil) is being used every year for producing electricity. However, power generation to the extent of 10 per cent is dependent on high-cost gas supplies. We are making efforts to access natural gas from other countries.

Now I shall discuss another fossil fuel, coal. Even though India has abundant quantities of coal, it is constrained to regional locations and has a high ash content, affecting the thermal efficiency of our power plants, and also there are environmental concerns. Thus, a movement towards energy independence would demand accelerated work in operationalizing the production of energy from the coal sector through integrated gasification and combined cycle route. In 2030, the total energy requirement would be 400,000 MW. At that time, the power generated from coal-based power plants would increase from the existing 67,000 MW to 200,000 MW. This would demand a significant build-up of thermal power stations and large-scale expansion of coal fields.

Changing structure of energy sources

The strategic goals for energy independence by 2030 would thus call for a shift in the structure of energy sources. Firstly, fossil fuel imports need to be minimized and secure access to be ensured. Maximum hydro and nuclear power potential should be tapped. The most significant aspect, however, would be that the power generated through renewable energy technologies may target 20 to 25 per cent against the present 5 per cent. It would be evident that for true energy independence, a major shift in the structure of energy sources from fossil to renewable energy sources is mandated.

Solar farms

Solar energy in particular requires unique, massive applications in the agricultural sector, where farmers need electricity exclusively in the daytime. This could be the primary demand driver for solar energy. Our farmers' demand for electric power today is significantly high to make solar energy economical on a large scale.

Shortages of water, both for drinking and farming operations, can be met by large-scale seawater desalination and pumping inland using solar energy, supplemented by biofuels wherever necessary.

The current high capital costs of solar power stations can be reduced by grid-locked 100 MW sized very large scale solar photovoltaic (VLSPV) or solar thermal power stations. In the very near future, breakthroughs in nanotechnologies promise significant increase in solar cell efficiencies from the current 15 per cent values to over 50 per cent levels. These would in turn reduce the cost of solar energy production. Our science laboratories should mount an R&D programme for developing high-efficiency CNT based photovoltaic cells.

We thus need to embark on a major national programme in solar energy systems and technologies, for both large, centralized applications as well as small, decentralized requirements concurrently, for applications in both rural and urban areas.

Nuclear energy

Nuclear power generation has been given a thrust by the use of uranium-based fuel. However there would be a requirement for a tenfold increase in nuclear power generation even to attain a reasonable degree of energy self-sufficiency for our country. Therefore it is essential to pursue the development of nuclear power using thorium, reserves of which are higher in the country. Technology development has to be accelerated for thorium-based reactors since the raw material for thorium is abundantly available in our country. Also, nuclear fusion research needs to be progressed with international cooperation to keep that option for meeting the large power requirement, at a time when fossil fuels get depleted.

Power from municipal waste

In the power generation sector of the energy economy, we need to fully use the technologies now available for generating power from municipal waste. Today, two plants are operational in India, each plant generating 6.5 MW of electric power. Studies indicate that as much as 5800 MW of power can be generated by setting up 900 electric power plants spread over different parts of the country which can be fuelled by municipal waste. The electric power generation and the creation of a clean environment are the twin advantages.

Power system loss reduction

Apart from generating power and running power stations efficiently without interruption, it is equally essential to transmit and distribute the power with minimum loss. The loss of power in transmission and distribution in our country is currently in the region of 30 to 40 per cent for a variety of reasons. Of about 1,000 billion units of electrical energy produced annually, only 600 billion units reach the consumer. This is the result of transmission loss and unaccounted loss. We need to take urgent action to bring down this loss to 15 per cent from 30–40 per cent by close monitoring of the losses, improving efficiency, and increasing the power factor through modern technology. By this one action alone we will be able to avoid the need for additional investment of around Rs 70,000 crore for establishing additional generating capacity.

Transportation sector

The transportation sector is the fastest growing energy consumer. It now consumes nearly 112 million tonnes of oil annually, and is critically important in our nation's economy and security. The complete substitution of oil imports for the transportation sector is the biggest and toughest challenge for India.

Use of biofuels

We have nearly 60 million hectares of wasteland, of which 30 million hectares are available for energy plantations like Jatropha. Once grown, the crop has a life of fifty years. Each acre will produce about 2 tonnes of biodiesel at about Rs 20 per litre. Biodiesel is carbon neutral and many valuable by-products flow from this agro-industry. Intensive research is needed to burn biofuel in internal combustion engines with high efficiency, and this needs to be an urgent R&D programme. India has a potential to produce nearly 60 million tonnes of biofuel annually, thus making a significant and important contribution to the goal of energy independence. Indian Railways has already taken a significant step by running two passenger locomotives (Thanjavur to Nagore section) and six trains of diesel multiple units (Tiruchirapalli to Lalgudi, Dindigul and Karur sections) with a 5 per cent blend of biofuel sourced from its in-house esterification plants. In addition, they have planted 75 lakh Jatropha saplings in railway land which is expected to give yields from the current year onwards. This is a pioneering example for many other organizations to follow.

Similarly many states in our country have energy plantations. What is needed is a full economic chain from farming, harvesting, extraction to esterification, blending and marketing. Apart from employment generation, biofuel has a significant potential to lead our country towards energy independence.

The other critical options are development of electric vehicles; hydrogen-based vehicles, electrification of railways and urban mass transportation.

Conclusion

By 2020 the nation should achieve comprehensive energy security through enhancement of our oil and gas exploration and production worldwide. By the year 2030, India should achieve energy independence through solar power and other forms of renewable energy; maximize the utilization of hydro and nuclear power and enhance the biofuel production through large scale energy plantations like Jatropha.

We need to evolve a comprehensive renewable energy policy for energy independence within a year. This should address all issues relating to generation of energy through wind, solar, geothermal, bio-mass and ocean resources. The nation should also work towards establishment of thorium-based reactors. Research and technology development of thorium-based reactors is one of the immediate requirements for realizing self-reliance in nuclear power generation and long-term energy security for the nation.

We should operationalize a 500 MW capacity power plant using integrated gasification and combined cycle route within the next three years from the existing pilot plant stage.

Biofuel research should be extended in collaboration with R&D laboratories, academic institutions and the automobile industry to make it a full-fledged fuel for the fleet running in the country in a timebound manner. This should lead to a mission mode integrated programme encompassing various ministries and industries. Also there is a need to formulate a comprehensive biofuel policy from research, development, production to marketing.

Energy security leading to energy independence is certainly possible and is within the capability of the nation. India has knowledge and natural resources; what we need is planned integrated missions to achieve the target in a timebound manner. Let us all work for self-sufficient environment friendly energy independence for the nation.

Electricity

When looking at the various energy sources we have discussed different ways of obtaining electricity. Electricity is the key to modern civilization. It is inconceivable to think of any of modern operational system that can run without electricity. If India has to bring the benefits of modern knowledge to all its citizens and introduce new opportunities for individuals to have a better life for themselves, the widespread availability of electricity is a must.

But while the utility sector has the responsibility to supply high quality uninterrupted power, it must also consciously encourage consumers to cut consumption, in an effort to reduce global warming and conserve the Earth's precious resources of energy fuels. It is with this purpose that new types of refrigerators, lighting systems, air cooling and heating systems, washing machines etc., which are more energy efficient, are being invented. There are now new types of light emitting diodes (LEDs) under large-scale experimentation which can provide the same intensity of light as a tube light or electric bulb but with far less power consumption (as low as 5 watts). The development of such products is one of the great scientific and social challenges of the twenty-first century.

Dr Kalam's thoughts on many aspects of energy and electricity form a part of many of his speeches. Here is an excerpt from his inaugural address at the fourteenth annual conference of the Indian Nuclear Society at Kalpakkam on 7 December 2003.

We should reinforce our gains in the agriculture, power (thermal, hydroelectric and non-conventional energy), ICT, industrial and education sectors, space, nuclear, and defence technologies, chemical, pharmaceutical and infrastructural industries, oil exploration and refining, and more importantly in the critical technologies.

When we are consolidating our strengths in all the areas energy and water are the primary inputs for all sustained developmental activity. For the last five decades we have gained strength in many critical areas including the development of nuclear technologies leading to nuclear energy. We have achieved a unique status of being the best performer in running nuclear power plants with 90 per cent capacity. The criteria for performance assessment have been based on availability, reliability, safe operation and the power plant practices followed.

Vision to mission

We need to evolve and develop specific integrated missions sector-wise to take the country forward on the path to self-sustaining development. These missions will provide the thrust for the realization of a developed India in a timebound manner. They will also provide large scale employment opportunity for the youth through creation of various types of industries and enhancement of the national infrastructure. In this gathering, I would like to discuss two important missions on energy and water security.

Power mission

As you are aware, for meeting the targets of developed India our generating capacity has to get tripled by 2020 from the existing 100,000 MW of power. This has got to be achieved through three different sources namely hydel capacity, nuclear power and non-conventional energy sources (primarily solar energy). The hydel capacity generated through interlinking of rivers is expected to contribute nearly 34,000 MW of power. Large-scale solar energy farms of 800–1000 MW capacity, a hundred in number, could contribute around 100,000 MW. The nuclear power plants should have a target of 50,000 MW of power. The balance has to be generated through the conventional thermal plants. The present nuclear power capacity of fourteen reactors which is 2,720 MW is expected to go up to 7,420 MW by 2010 with the completion of nine reactors which are now in progress. Eventually as per present plans BARC is expecting the capacity to be 20,000 MW by 2020. Hence, there is a need to plan right from now to increase this capacity by another 30,000 MW.

Our modest uranium resources can support the generation of about 15,000 MW through the present generation of pressurized heavy water reactors (PHWR) which consume less than 1 per cent of our uranium resource. The recycle of PU-239 along with balance uranium in depleted form to second stage fast breeder reactors (FBRs) will provide us access to about 130 times more energy potential from our limited uranium reserve. Finally we have to fall back on waste thorium resource (about one-third of the world's total thorium resource) for our energy security. For this we have to introduce thorium in the blanket zone of second stage FBRs at an appropriate growth level of installed nuclear capacity. This would enable us to build inventory of U-233 (from thorium) for use in the third stage of our nuclear power programme based on yet another type of fast breeder reactor using Th-U233 MOX fuel in the core.

India possesses pilot scale experience in the thorium U-233 fuel cycle including experience in building the research reactor Kamini. However we need to master all the technologies at the front end and the back end of the thorium U-233 fuel cycle at a plant scale to address all the technological problems involved in thorium utilization. We should plan to build the first thorium fuel based advance heavy water reactor with a capacity of 1,000 MW immediately.

Water

Earlier, we have discussed how water is the essence of life and how very limited resources of usable water are available on Earth. The challenge before us is to conserve water, reduce its use wherever possible, and to recycle and reuse water.

About 85 per cent of the water usage in our country is in the agriculture sector. Industries account for 10 per cent, and domestic use is only 5 per cent. Our usage of water for agriculture is very wasteful. We still use the flooding method which was used centuries ago. We also throw away the used agricultural water, with its chemicals and organic matter, as waste water. These in turn pollute ponds, lakes and rivers. It is very essential to reuse used agricultural water by recycling it after removing the harmful chemicals and organic matter. There are some waste recycling plants that clean and reuse municipal water, but we do not have these facilities yet in the agriculture sector. Public opinion needs to be shaped based on the science of recycling and reuse. The availability of clean water for all will greatly reduce and even eliminate the spread of most diseases.

In addition to recycling and reusing, it is important to significantly reduce the consumption of water in the agriculture sector. Instead of using the antiquated flooding method, we should use drip irrigation and sprinklers. Drip irrigation is a very efficient means of water utilization. A small rugged tube is laid all along the field with small holes at select points. The holes release waterdrops slowly at the bottom of the plant. The plant thus has plenty of water the whole day. The whole process can be controlled by a small computer which can open and close the taps at regular intervals, thus further controlling the water use. Drip irrigation is also not dependent on the vagaries of the monsoon and regularizes agricultural production.

However, because of the widespread rain-fed open field agriculture that is prevalent in India, operated mostly by poor and marginal farmers who are not able to invest even in a water pump, advanced techniques like drip irrigation are not used widely. The initiative has to be taken by the government. In areas where the government has built good irrigation canals and dams e.g. Punjab and Haryana, water is available and is cheap. We need to set up a modern scientific irrigation infrastructure in other parts of India that are rain-fed and thus suffer from vagaries of the monsoon. If we are able to do this, India will be free from water scarcity and from dependence on the monsoon for its agriculture.

Dr Kalam has often stressed the need to interlink our rivers for the prevention of floods and droughts. This would also lead to a more efficient irrigation system and better access to water. He referred to this project in his Independence Day speech as President in 2005.

Rainfall and floods are annual features in many parts of the country. Instead of thinking of interlinking rivers only at times of flood and drought, it is time that we implement this programme with a great sense of urgency. We need to make an effort to overcome various hurdles in our way to the implementation of this major project. I feel that it has the promise of freeing the country from the endless cycle of floods and droughts.

Other aspects of recycling and reusing water, for the industry and domestic sectors, are crucial as well, but these are required more in order to have a pollution-free environment.

Dr Kalam's speech at Kalpakkam on 7 December 2003 indicates the great urgency of water conservation and management with a view to the future.

Global crisis of water

Today, with a global population of 6 billion, only 3 billion have access to limited or perhaps a satisfactory supply of water. It is estimated that 33 per cent of the world population has no access to sanitation and 17 per cent has no access to safe water. By 2025 the world population is going to rise to 8 billion but only 1 billion will have sufficient water. Two billion (25 per cent) will have no access to safe water. Five billion (62 per cent) will have no access to sanitation. We should collectively find a solution to this problem.

==============================

Unlike other essentials like food and energy, there is no scope for producing more water than we have on Earth. So we need to act on a war footing to reduce water usage, conserve our existing resources of water through initiatives like rainwater harvesting, recycle and reuse water for multiple purposes, improve our waste water management and reduce the percentage of waste water that we dispose of. To achieve this, more than scientists, engineers and government persons, the intervention and participation of civil society is required.

Chapter 9

HEALTH CARE

So far we have looked at things external to the human body; we shall now turn our gaze inward. All the resources available from nature and the benefits of technology are enjoyable only when we have good health.

In a broad sense, the health of Indians has improved tremendously over the past six decades. In the 1940s the average life expectancy of an Indian was about thirty years; it is now about sixty-six years. That fact that we now have about 110 million senior citizens (above sixty years of age) speaks volumes about the overall health situation. This achievement is because of food security, a certain amount of primary health care being available to all, advances in medical diagnostic equipment, and most importantly many recent advances in the pharmaceuticals sector that have made crucial medicines available and accessible to all.

India has a proud heritage in medicine. Charaka, the great medicine man, and Susruta, the great surgeon of his time, were well ahead of their contemporaries in the world. Indian knowledge in medicinal plants spread to many other countries. Ayurveda was a well-established science that has been in existence for millennia. In addition there was the Siddha school of medicine. With the Mughals came Unani medicine. In addition, there were folk treatments and remedies practised in villages and also by tribal groups. Some of these are available even now. Dr Kalam's elder brother Mohammed Muthu Meera Maraicayar (now about ninety-four years old) lives in Rameswaram and has a deep knowledge of the rich heritage of folk medicines practiced by his ancestors; the family's medical knowledge has been captured by his daughter Dr Nazima Maraicayar in a book. Now there is worldwide scientific interest in many of our traditional medical practices. There is also a separate government ministry called Ayush to look after the preservation and growth of Ayurveda, Yoga, Unani, Siddha and homeopathic systems of alternate health care.

Medical science today is a combination of many specialized fields like life sciences, biochemistry, biophysics, bio-medical engineering and biotechnology. We will not go into details of these fields of study, but look at some of their practical uses in health care today.

Preventive health care

Most of us think health care is only relevant when we become ill; there is no concept of prevention. In fact, many diseases can be prevented if our personal hygiene is taken care of and our local environment is kept clean, free of garbage and stagnant pools of water. The availability and use of clean water, free of harmful chemicals, bacteria and organic matter, would sharply reduce the outbreak of many diseases in India. For example many Indians suffer chronically from diarrhoea and gastroenteritis; these are waterborne diseases resulting from use of unclean water.

Similarly many of us do not take care of the cleanliness of the food we eat. Many meat and fish products are not stored properly. Sometimes the animals themselves are diseased. Many vegetables are grown on soils that have poor sanitary conditions. They are also used without being washed properly, and some bacteria can penetrate the skins of the vegetables. In general the old Indian habit of overcooking food and boiling milk serve to remove at least some bacterial contamination, but it also takes away precious nutritional contents of food. Better hygiene can come partly from general facilities made available by public authorities (including clean public toilets) and partly from our own learning and awareness as well as civic sense.

Nutrition is another important aspect of health. A large number of Indian women (about 40 per cent of the female population) are anaemic, i.e. the cells containing iron oxide (called red blood cells) are less than the required number in their blood. Iron oxides carry oxygen which the blood provides to the billions of cells in the body. When red blood cells are less in number than they should be, the cells are deficient in growth. In general an anaemic person will be weak and will not be able to resist many bacterial and viral attacks. The human body has to fight against many microbes both inside the body and outside. There are immune systems in the body to detect and to fight the 'enemies'. But if a person is anaemic, his/her immunity is low. Most cases of anaemia can be prevented if a person eats a good nutritious diet. Iron is easily obtained from liver, bone marrow etc.; it is also obtained from many vegetables like spinach and fruits like prunes. Again it is not enough just to have these in one's diet; they should be cooked carefully to ensure that the nutrients are not destroyed in the cooking process.

There is a lot that needs to be learnt by Indians in terms of good nutritional practices and cooking methods. Traditional habits have to be partially modified to adapt to modern scientific knowledge. While a lot is written about nutrition in magazines and newspapers and also reported in the electronic media, there are many distortions of scientific facts. Commercial interests prompt manufacturers to make exaggerated claims for their products. It is important for knowledgeable experts to engage with the subject and spread the correct information.

While disease diagnostics and medical care are important, we should remember that as a nation we can be healthy only when we prevent diseases and make each individual fit. The responsibility for this belongs with each of us: we must exercise regularly and lead a healthy lifestyle to attain minimum fitness levels.*

Diagnostic facilities

One critical component of modern medical practice is diagnostics, commonly called medical tests. Blood tests and urine and stool tests are often the first steps in diagnosing health problems. Electrocardiograms (ECG) show the functioning of the heart and X-rays can show even hairline cracks in bones. But X-rays cannot image softer parts of the body like the lungs, liver, spleen, pancreas, kidneys or the brain. For these, ultrasound imaging systems are used. In order to penetrate through bones and to study brain damage one has to use a magnetic resonance imaging (MRI) scanner.

Laboratory testing systems, ultrasounds and X-rays have now become quite economical and very compact, so much so that they can all be fitted inside an ordinary bus, in addition to a diagnostic table and a fitted 15 KVA diesel electric generator. These are the components of a mobile diagnostic centre, which is vital for India whose remote corners are bereft of hospitals and deprived of medical care. As part of the follow-up to the Vision 2020 study, TIFAC designed a mobile diagnostic centre, which was fitted into a bus and visited villages on a regular basis. What was found in the Vision 2020 study was that most doctors and primary health centres in the remote parts suffer from a lack of these basic diagnostic facilities. Naturally this handicaps the doctors in further medical treatment as well. The National Rural Health Mission (NRHM) has now adopted the concept of mobile diagnostic units and plans to have one in every district so that the local people can benefit from modern medical technology.

---

*We would like to refer readers to the chapter on health care for all in our book *India 2020: A Vision for the New Millennium*, which contains the combined knowledge and wisdom of many health care practitioners in India.

Though modern medical knowledge and capabilities are high, medical science is still developing and new research may make diagnosis and treatment even easier. The access to medical experts in remote areas (non-existent at present) may become possible in the future with the use of broadband communication systems that can provide full medical imagery and information about a rural patient to a city-based specialist in an instant. Dr Kalam has high hopes for such tele-medicine facilities. The TIFAC mobile unit in Uttarakhand has the necessary provisions for computers and a communications interface.

The emergence of nanotechnology and stem cell research may bring about many new medical capabilities in the coming decades, especially in treating cancer at an early stage, cleaning up arterial blockages, repairing liver and brain damage, and so on.

Stem cell research, genetic engineering and neuroscience

We all know that the human body is made up of billions of cells. Not all cells are the same. During the long evolution of life from single cell organisms to complex mammals, human body cells have acquired many specialized features. For instance, the cells of the bones and bone marrow are completely different from the muscle cells of the biceps, and skin cells are completely different again. The function that a body part has to perform strongly determines the structure of its cells.

The cells in our body do not live as long as we do. They have a short life: they grow, perform their functions, and die, and new cells replace them. The life span of a cell can range from a few days to years; their change cycles are very different too. Brain cells, called neurons, grow to full size in our childhood; after that there is only decay, and no replacement.

At the growth phase of human life (the embryo) all cells start off as general purpose cells called stem cells. As the embryo grows, specialization sets in. Most cells (called committed stem sells) develop in particular ways to form body parts, multiply, and are replaced by cells of the same type. But some stem cells, known as uncommitted stem cells, are for general application, and can serve any body part.

If the general purpose stem cells can be generated in large numbers and injected into the damaged region of a grown human body, they can stick there and grow further, changing to the kind of cells with specific features required for that region. This is the basis of stem cell research, which is one of the most important scientific activities being undertaken in the world today.

Another area that holds great promise is genetic engineering. Genes carry vital information about how different features of the body will develop. Defects in genes cause some genetic (inherited) diseases. If the genes can be re-engineered, the health of mankind can improve dramatically. But this is an area which has to be pursued with great caution.

Another emerging area of medical research is neuroscience. Traditionally, human psychology has been studied by looking at behaviour patterns. But with the availability of various forms of bio-medical scanners and sensors that can measure and map neural activity in the brain, scientific observations about various mental activities have increased. Such researches are aimed at curing many brain-defect induced diseases such as Alzheimer's disease. They are also aimed at a better understanding of the way in which the brain functions. India has an institute in Bengaluru and a dedicated centre in Gurgaon that conduct research in this area.

Differently enabled persons

The word 'disabled' is no longer used when describing persons who have problems of attention, conversation or cognition when compared to the 'normal' standards set by the majority. The phrases 'physically challenged', 'mentally challenged', 'visually challenged' etc. are not in use any longer either. A new vocabulary has emerged putting the situation of such individuals in a positive perspective.

Differently enabled persons are often extraordinarily excellent in certain skills, maybe in capturing large amounts of detail that 'normal' people cannot, or in having an exceptionally good memory capability. Dyslexia is a kind of different enabling which was brought to popular attention with the film *Taare Zameen Par*. Autism is another condition that affects people. Advances in genetic sciences and neurosciences are likely to reveal many new findings about differently enabled people.

Some children and their parents also face challenges arising from birth defects in hearing, vision, defects in limbs especially through polio attacks, and several other genetically inherited defects. The number of such children in India runs into several tens of millions. It is a big health care challenge.

In his speeches Dr Kalam has touched on several elements of health care. In a talk given at the National Institute of Pharmaceutical Education and Research (NIPER) at SASA Nagar, Punjab on 29 September 2003, he recalled TIFAC's Vision 2020 report on health care and summarized the main challenges before us.

A report on 'Health Care in India' has been prepared by a panel of leading doctors and medical technologists in the country. It reports the typical problems facing us for two decades in health care and possible solutions.

The expert team has identified three major diseases viz. tuberculosis, HIV and water-borne diseases which we need to combat urgently by the next decade. The other diseases which need our attention are cardiovascular diseases, neuro-psychiatric disorders, renal diseases and hypertension, gastrointestinal disorders, eye disorders, genetic diseases, accidents and trauma. We should see how the advancement in technology could be put to use to improve the health care system of the country. Such an effort will make cost-effective medical technology and devices available and accessible to all the citizens of our country. This will contribute to the nation's progress as a strong body and sound minds are essential to accomplish anything.

The report has brought out many dimensions of health care problems in our country. The vision of providing affordable and effective health care to our entire population goes much beyond the capability of any individual, institution or organization. Technology is an important tool to give fast health care and we have to use it. This vision has to become a multi-organizational mission leading to the generation of thousands of goal-oriented projects. These projects will have to be supported and nurtured not only by the government, but also by our industry and philanthropic organizations. The most important ingredient of such a multi-organizational mission will be the leadership decentralized and yet linked together.

The interfacing between medical science and various other technologies has given rise to numerous techniques, both curative and investigative, and has provided the research worker with numerous tools to pry into the working of various physiological functions right up to the molecular levels. Developments in bio-technology and molecular biology have now made it possible not only to design drugs for specific properties but also to deliver them to the specific sites where they are most required. Newer imaging techniques have now made it possible to obtain real time images of the various organs at a physiological and biological level and hence the right treatment is possible. Medical research will lead to not only the ability to identify the genes that cause disease but also correct the defects through gene therapy. Recent breakthroughs in stem cell research are likely to lead to the regeneration of diseased organs.

The role of genes in heart diseases and strokes is now universally accepted. The apo-B gene is responsible for cholesterol management in the body. Molecular biology will also have a clear impact on the science and practice of psychiatry in the near future.

———————————

Dr Kalam also spoke about advanced materials for dental care at the World Congress on Prosthondontics in New Delhi on 26 November 2003.

———————————

Advances in materials like composites, polymers, ceramics and fibre-reinforced composites have found their place in dentistry. By using laser technology, emerging nanotechnology, tele-radiology, digital imagery and virtual reality etc., the rehabilitation process will be modelled and energized for providing customized prosthodontics treatment. Scientists from genetic engineering are working towards development of individual tissue organs through the use of stem cells. When any organ of the human body can be rehabilitated using an individual's own stem cells, it will not be far off when we can see reconditioning of the teeth through stem cells used for promoting the growth of tissues and bones. Intensive research is needed for realizing this breakthrough. Very soon we may see a person having real natural teeth either replanted or repaired in place of the missing teeth.

There is a need to network the dental centres, particularly research centers located in different parts of the country, to generate a clinical database which will be useful for research. It can also be made available on the Internet for sharing of information and academic research leading to path-breaking findings. This type of connectivity will enable research on different dental problems pertaining to different regions in the country. Also the clinical database of one particular surgeon will be available to other dental surgeons for deciding on the line of treatments for similar cases. The region-specific research database could be used for suggesting preventive medicine or preventive care to the local community based on doctors' experiences. We need to have a centralized database on Indian dental problems, cases, remedies and solutions. Also it will enable detection of related diseases arising out of water and other environmental factors in a particular region. This could help proper treatment of water and provide better health for the community as a whole. Better use of tele-medicine for dental care in the remote villages will enable the doctors to examine the patients using intra-oral x-rays through digital sensors and provide consultancies through virtual dental clinics which can provide knowledge to the field centres.

In different parts of the country, there are many traditional practitioners who are providing health care products from herbal plants in the form of powders for dental care. Still many people in the villages make use of these products and some of them are able to maintain sound dental health. My father lived for 103 years. Up to the age of ninety-eight, all his teeth were intact. He had not gone to any dental clinic throughout his life. Only during his later years I realized that he was using neem sticks for brushing his teeth both in the morning and before going to bed. This practice is slowly vanishing because of the aggressive marketing of modern medical products. There is a need to identify some areas of excellence and carry out systematic research in the area using the knowledge base of the traditional practitioners. A case study could be conducted about the use of neem tree material as a cost-effective solution for promoting dental care in the villages. Apart from neem, efficacy of ingredients like cloves and herbs could also be studied for use in dental paste and powder. We need to examine them more critically and make use of the traditional knowledge base for the welfare of people. This could be done by having a workshop specially dedicated to assembling the traditional system practitioners and having a constructive discussion.

At the inauguration of the Peterson Cancer Centre in Chennai on 19 June 2003, Dr Kalam spoke on some of the salient aspects of how cancer develops and how we can combat it.

———————————————

Cancer, unlike many other diseases that come from external factors like infections, life style and other environmental and physiological stressors, emanate from within the cell. The life software embedded in the DNA material gets mutated and starts growing in a way that is not in line with the cells around. Life turns against itself. The disease becomes unfathomable when it happens too early.

Sometime back, I met one gentleman whose six-year-old grandchild was on periodic blood transfusion for thalassemia. The permanent solution, doctors told me, was a bone marrow transplant. The bone marrow of the child was not matching even between siblings and the parents. Unmatched bone marrow transplant is not done in India, I was told, and even in the West it is done experimentally. I met the child who is unaware of the time bomb that is ticking inside him. I prayed for him, for this was the only thing I could do. Today, standing before this gathering of cancer experts, I think I must share with you my concern for these and other patients who live under the shadow of uncertain life. What can we do to strengthen the doctors' capabilities in such a situation? In India, there are less than 100 beds for BMT. This has to be increased in multiple hospitals. Stem cells are the live source for bone marrow production. It is indeed only in the research phase.

Stem cell research

Newer knowledge emerging out of research on stem cells from abroad and India has to be taken note of and studied. In fact, regenerative medicine is fast getting established as a complete branch of medical science. The embryo starts out as a mass of undifferentiated cells, which then divide, multiply and go down differential paths to take the shape of various tissues and organs of the body. The mechanisms that underline this orderly process of differentiation is fast getting understood at the laboratory level. And the state-of-the-art research in this area holds the promise of regenerating tissue that malfunctions due to injury, age, disease or genetic abnormality. A Japanese team has successfully created stem cells from the embryonic cells of mice to create cells that secrete insulin and glucagon, two hormones normally made by the pancreas. Whether large volumes of cells can be produced from stem cells is yet to be seen. I hope that the day is not far when the six-year-old boy I met will get a tailor-made bone marrow out of stem cells to survive for the next sixty years and beyond. For such a mission, BMT and stem cell production are vital. Research for stem cells and development of BMT are important needs. This hospital can be an interface to take the benefit of research to the patient.

A new approach

Cancer treatment needs a new mindset. I would like to share a vision of 'patients deserve the best' here. I will organize my thoughts into four areas that can lead to a road map of a collaborative work between different clinical experts, medical and other research institutions, industries and other organizations. There is a need to create cancer awareness and taking cancer diagnostics to detect cancers in the early stage. The therapeutic procedures need to be made affordable and accessible, thereby minimizing travel of patients for treatment and follow-up. A clinical database network can be established to effectively tackle the cancer with a long-term prevention–rehabilitation perspective. Finally, focused efforts are needed to derive practical clinical applications from the findings of the human genome project.

Futuristic goals can be set among cancer hospitals and

research institutions. Diagnostic and treatment results need to be discussed and analysed. Diagnostic accuracy, response to treatment, cure results need to be discussed among similar cancer cure institutions. Then the national capability of cancer cure will enhance. Citizens will be thankful to the healers.

Optimization of chemotherapy

Chemotherapy often destroys healthy cells together with the intended cancerous ones. An industrial firm in our country has developed algorithms describing interaction between normal cells, malignant cells and nutrients. The algorithms also take into account the pharmaco-kinetics of the drug. Together with inputs on patients' age, height and weight and the type and volume of the tumour, the mathematical model can design an optimal drug schedule minimizing side effects. The type and volume of tumour can be automatically deduced from the CT or MRI scans. This is a good example of how advances in many disciplines of science such as biomedical engineering, image processing, control systems, mathematical modelling and pharmacology are helping in developing better and more effective treatments for cancer patients.

Here are Dr Kalam's thoughts on another important area of advances in health care: brain research. What follows are extracts from Dr Kalam's address at the National Brain Research Centre, Manesar on 16 December 2003.

By the end of this century there would be a strong trend towards convergence of human thinking with the world of machine intelligence that the human species initially created. When there would no longer be any clear distinction between humans and computers, how would the molecular biologists help us to retain the supremacy of man over machines? Computers are going to give us a challenge. Not only the biologists and bio-technologists, but the entire scientific community would have the great responsibility of keeping mankind above the man-made computers. Unfortunately, the creativity and imagination components of the human brain have not been fully explored and utilized. Even the human genome research has enormous application of software in understanding the complex sequence of gene profiles and its relationship to human health and disease. With a wide ethnic diversity of our nation, a unique database can be created with special application of pharmacogenetics (personalized medicine) for focusing health care delivery.

I understand that by proper stimulation of the brain, we should be able to regenerate the lost neurons and thereby make the brain function better. By intra-cranial self-stimulation in rats, more neurons get created and it improves the learning ability and faster cure for injuries. Enriched environment is also capable of generating neurons using natural stimulation. Electrical stimulation needs insertion of electrodes in the brain and it can be highly pinpointed. We have to resolve ethical issues for resorting to this treatment among human beings. We may also try to explore the application of electromagnetic stimulation non-invasively to stimulate the dormant neurons of the specific brain areas. Use of stem cells, neuronal transplantation and nerve growth factors may also be considered.

Epilepsy research

Incidence of epilepsy in the country is fairly high. Present treatment for epilepsy using surgical or pharmacological control and management of the episodes involves quietening the hyperactive parts of the brain neurons. Is it possible to locate the specific focal point responsible for the seizure through neural imaging by MRI or Positron Emission Tomography (PET)?

Scientists working in nanotechnology can work with brain researchers to develop a small device which can be implanted in the brain close to the focal point which can buffer spurious high-intensity spikes and create a near-normal brain function thereby improving the quality of life of these patients. Can we target specific nano-tracers to the epileptic foci to carry out a similar function? It is quite a challenge which the centre can consider.

Deriving behavioural and aptitude patterns

The complex nature of brain functioning engulfs in itself answers to many problems that need to be fully understood for human development. The structural and functional mapping of the human brain would help in scientific analysis of human behaviour. Through rigorous and extensive research findings, if it becomes possible to analyse behavioural tendencies and derive an inclination or aptitude pattern of a person, especially at an early age, it will help the person to opt for that field or area, for optimum utilization of the human potential and talent. It will also enable early detection of negative emotions and projection of concealed destructive tendencies in a child, which can be dealt with by providing various clinical and psychological treatments and ensuring a conducive atmosphere for strong physical and mental growth of the child. Such balanced and healthy development of one's emotional intelligence will lead to the evolution of a truly enlightened citizen.

Coming now to vascular diseases, here are Dr Kalam's thoughts on the subject from his speech at the sixth biannual International Congress of the Asian Vascular Society, Bengaluru on 5 November 2004.

I understand that vascular surgery deals with diseases of all the blood vessels (arteries, veins and lymphatics) in the body, except those in the brain which are dealt with by neurosurgeons and those around the heart which come under cardiac surgery. Though the term cardiovascular surgery was commonly used in the past, now vascular surgery has emerged as a separate super-speciality. A vascular surgeon deals exclusively with the treatment of blood vessel diseases, whether it requires medical therapy, surgery or newer minimally invasive endovascular procedures.

I can visualize the human body functions due to the network of arteries and veins connecting all the organs of the body. The healthy condition of this vascular network is essential for the smooth functioning of all the organs which makes the entire body healthy. How do we ensure that the network is seamless and fully functional, that appears to be the challenge before the vascular experts.

The occurrence of vascular disease is increasing rapidly particularly in the Indian community. Multi-dimensional solutions are available for management of the diseases according to my discussion with experts. The solutions include medicinal treatment using statins which lowers the cholesterol in the blood by reducing the production of cholesterol by the liver. Statins block the enzyme in the liver responsible for making excess cholesterol. However one has to be careful about the side effects and take adequate precautions while treating the patients. The second is through angiography and angioplasty using stents. If the vein blockage is severe, surgical intervention will be necessary. The recent advances in medical research have opened several new opportunities for treating vascular disorders.

Stem cell therapy for future heart ailments

Newer knowledge emerging out of research on stem cells from abroad and India has to be taken note of and studied. Drawing tens of thousands of stem cells—immature cells that are capable of transforming themselves into almost any kind of tissues— from the suffering patient and injecting them into the heart to stimulate heart repair is a possibility. In one case, it is reported that the pumping efficiency has increased from 25 to 40 per cent over a period of four months. In 2003, successful stem cell procedures that resulted in a measurable boost in blood pumping capacity have increased substantially in many countries across the globe. This holds a big promise for effective heart repair for ailing people. Vascular surgeons must see whether stem cells can help in curing all kinds of vascular diseases.

There is a need to propagate the importance of appropriate food habits and life style among the urban population to combat the situation of increased occurrence of heart ailments. Hospitals in the country should take proactive steps to counsel their clients in a family atmosphere for ensuring reduction in this number in the years to come. Another feature that has been noticed is that there is a competition between cardiologists and surgeons in treating heart cases. The ideal practice should be to provide only the minimum essential treatment instead of going in for surgical intervention as a routine management of the disease.

It has been reported that the repeated occurrence of heart ailments is caused by diet, smoking, and lack of exercise and uncontrolled diabetes. All these factors can be controlled by an appropriate life style intervention.

Here are Dr Kalam's thoughts on eye care, transmitted through a video conference on 14 August 2004.

You may be aware that a Health Care Technology vision document was evolved as part of Technology Vision 2020 a few years back. Prof. M.S. Valiathan led the team in evolving the health care vision document. A number of experts in the area of ophthalmology were involved in the task teams. Many important issues were brought into the document. It is said that in India, a minimum of 20 million people out of the billion-strong population are visually handicapped, while 25 million people are partially visually handicapped. The population growth coupled with increase in life expectancy will only lead to an increase in the number of blind and visually handicapped people. In 80 per cent of the cases, the cause of blindness is due to cataract. The other causes have been identified as diseases of the cornea, glaucoma, diabetes and other vitreo retinal disorders, Vitamin-A deficiency etc. The expert team identified preventive technologies, diagnostic technologies and curative corrective technologies. One of the major recommendations is to develop eye lasers with slit lamps for post-glaucoma and cataract patients' treatment, and large-scale production of cost effective Vitamin-A tablets. Recently, laser treatment for diabetic retinopathy to arrest eye bleeding has been added. Above all, education and management systems for eye care and also creating a human feeling to increase large numbers of eligible eye donors have to be generated.

Stem cell use for restoration of vision

The recent identification and characterization of progenitors with stem cell properties has opened new avenues that may be useful for treating functional impairments caused by the death of a specific cell population. Stromal and neuronal degeneration are the causes of debilitating visual impairment associated with many ocular diseases such as degenerative diseases of the cornea, retinitis pigmentosa (RP), age-related macular degeneration (AMD) and glaucoma. The stem cells may help restore vision in a patient who has these diseases by repopulating or rescuing the damaged ocular surface cells or retinal cells from further degeneration. The stem cells can be used for two different but complimentary ways to treat the degenerative diseases of the eye.

1. **Cell replacement therapy:** Cell replacement therapy exploits the plasticity of stem cells progenitors to replace cells and repair tissue damage by diseases or injury.
2. **Ex-vivo gene therapy:** Ex-vivo gene therapy could be used effectively as a neuro-protective strategy to prevent retinal cell loss in retinitis pigmentosa (RP), age-related muscular degeneration (AMD) and terminal stages of glaucoma.

Speaking on the efforts to combat glaucoma at the South East Asia Glaucoma Conference on 1 December 2006, Dr Kalam said:

Glaucoma is a silent disease of the eye, and the most important clinical sign is rise of intra-ocular pressure. It is estimated that over 65 million people are affected by glaucoma worldwide. Because symptoms appear very late, only half of the affected individuals are aware of the disease. There are two adult forms of glaucoma: open angle glaucoma and narrow angle glaucoma. Studies from India, Singapore and China have suggested that Asians suffer more from narrow angle glaucoma compared to other populations who suffer from open angle glaucoma. Glaucoma has been identified as a priority ocular disease requiring urgent measures of intervention to decrease the burden of blindness in the Right to Sight by Vision 2020 initiative.

The treatment of glaucoma begins with early diagnosis. While traditional means of diagnosing and monitoring the treatment was by measuring intra-ocular pressure, glaucoma researchers have realized that early defects can be demonstrated by plotting the field of vision and through primary damage, which occurs in retinal neural tissue around the optic nerve head. A variety of devices are now available to accurately and reproducibly measure the field and the retinal nerve fibre changes in glaucoma. It is essential to equip eye care centres with these measurement devices, particularly mobile clinics, so that they can use it for screening people in rural areas.

Treatment methodologies

Primary open angle glaucoma is mostly treated by medications. Primary narrow angle glaucoma is treated with laser iridotomy. Advanced stages of both open and closed angle glaucoma are treated by surgery. During the last few years there has been a marked change in glaucoma therapy due to the availability of superior intra-ocular pressure lowering agents that can be applied only once or twice a day so that patients are better compliant. However, I understand the cost of the drops is quite high. Specialists assembled here should work out strategies in partnership with pharma companies to bring down the cost of the drops for glaucoma medication.

Challenges

The challenge in glaucoma management is proper diagnosis at the appropriate time. Since narrow angle glaucoma is more prevalent in the Asian population, a simple test like gonioscopy that estimates the configuration of the anterior chamber angle will go a long way in detecting this form of glaucoma early. This is important since a simple and cost-effective laser treatment such as laser iridotomy can cure the glaucoma. My doctor friends say that doctors may sometimes want to monitor the intra-ocular pressure on an hourly basis, and doing it the conventional way is cumbersome. Would a device or probe be possible which could be inserted? Here is a challenge that should attract biomedical engineers and would be of great use for specialists. I firmly believe that learning gonioscopy must be made part of the ophthalmology curriculum for all eye specialists irrespective of their super-specialization.

Future direction

Glaucoma causes retinal neuronal dysfunction. Future glaucoma therapy should be directed to prevent, delay or reverse decay of the retinal ganglion cells and axons. Functional genomics and proteomics are likely to play a pivotal role in early detection of glaucoma.

The recent identification and characterization of progenitors with stem cell properties has opened new avenues that may be useful for treating functional impairments caused by the death of specific cell populations due to glaucoma. Stem cells may help restore vision in patients who have glaucoma by repopulating or rescuing damaged cells. Stem cells can also be used for terminal stages of glaucoma. A few of our ophthalmologists are already working in stem cell therapy. Gene therapy approach is applicable to either lower the intra-ocular pressure or protect retinal ganglion cells. This approach could reprogramme the target cells by transferring genetic material into them so that they lower intra-ocular pressure physiologically. Another promising therapy is the use of nanotechnology for targeted delivery of small-molecule therapeutic agents to the back of the eye.

———————————————————

Dr Kalam made an important point in his address at the sixty-fifth annual meeting of the All India Opthalmological Society in Hyderabad on 1 February 2007.

———————————————————

In my opinion the best time to begin detection of eye problems is early in life. The school is the ideal place. The teachers must be trained to measure eyesight so that they could seek help of ophthalmologists immediately. The members of the All India Ophthalmological Society can institute a training programme in their districts to train the teachers who can periodically test the children every year and seek professional advice if they find any child with vision difficulty. They can also train NSS volunteers, NCC cadets and scouts and guides in their region, who can become ambassadors of ophthalmologists in their districts.

On the subject of deafness, Dr Kalam had this to say at the third Cochlear Implant Group of India Conference in New Delhi on 5 November 2005.

My experience with cochlear implants

When I visited Vikram hospital in Coimbatore a few years back, I realized technological intervention is possible for bringing back hearing to the deaf and dumb children by implanting a device called the cochlear implant. Dr Aruna Viswanathan and her team demonstrated to me the whole process of implanting the device and the subsequent training procedure for the children. I saw four-year-old deaf and dumb children. After one of month of implanting and training they spoke out a few words legibly. After six months of computer-aided training, I have seen the children speaking normally. This touching scene moved me. I felt that I have to work to bring the cost of cochlear implants down, so that thousands and thousands of children in India and abroad can afford to have this device and lead a normal life. That is why I am with you today.

The status of hearing impairment

As per recent statistics, the number of people with profound hearing disability in India is about 1 million. In addition, there are over 1.2 million people with severe hearing disability, 0.9 million people with moderate hearing disability and 7.1 million people with very mild hearing disability. The medical community, social institutions and corporate houses have the task of restoring the disability of nearly 10 million people with the support of the government. The severe, moderate and mild category disability can be treated using conventional and digital hearing aids. Many ENT specialists spread across the country are doing this to a certain extent. But this has got to be intensified in the remote rural areas where people with disability suffer silently. Can we remove their pain?

Cochlear implants

Regarding the profound hearing disability, treatment is undertaken only in a very few medical institutions since it needs a special device called the cochlear implant, which I described to you earlier. When the child doesn't have the hearing capacity it leads to dumbness. A cochlear implant coupled with computer-aided training helps the deaf and dumb individuals to regain near-normal hearing/speaking capabilities. Basically it is bypassing the damaged inner ear portion by replacing its functions with an electronic system having an external microphone, a speech processing circuit, a transmitter and a receiver. The receiver is implanted below the ear. The receiver has an electrode, which is inserted into the cochlear portion of the ear. The speech processor processes the input audio signals and converts them into electrical signals in various channels. The transmitter transmits these signals to the implant's multi-channel electrode, which terminates in various points of the cochlea.

The latest cochlear implant technology, contour advance, recently introduced in India, is specifically designed to protect the small and delicate cochlea structures during surgery. This helps to preserve any residual hearing. Its curved shape also provides more focused stimulation of the hearing nerve for better quality outcomes. The further research in cochlear implants must lead to design and production of cochlear implants which will need minimum invasive procedures for fitment.

Indian experience in cochlear implants

The fitment of cochlear implants for treating the profound hearing impaired cases started in India in the year 1995. In the beginning, there used to be five or ten cases treated each year. Today, due to the awareness created by various institutions we are able to fit 150 implants a year. I am happy to know that among the hundred and fifty fitted, Army hospitals account for nearly seventy. In the last one decade we have treated nearly 750 cases in all. That means we are able to reach only 0.075 per cent of the affected population in the country. There has been continuous improvement in the cochlear implants produced by international manufacturers and the cost of implants has also been going up. How do we reach all the people affected by profound hearing disability? This is what this conference must address. Only then will we be able to achieve the goal of providing hearing and speech for all.

Dr Kalam has suggested a number of missions to reach such implants to all citizens. These require some initial investments and above all good programme management.

Finally, on autism, a neurological condition that hampers the normal functioning of the brain in children who are affected and which poses a challenge to parents as well as medical practitioners in terms of correct handling, Dr Kalam had this to say at the inauguration of the International Conference on Autism in New Delhi on 13 September 2006.

I have been studying the problems of mentally challenged children. There are many variants that mentally challenged people face and these include:

a. Attention deficit and disruptive behaviour disorders
b. Autism

c. Learning and communication disorders
d. Mood disorders
e. Schizophrenia
f. Cerebral palsy
g. Substance abuse

Within variants, research and study can establish a common thread. The subject of discussion today is autism.

Autism and a reason for hope

Autism is a complex developmental disability that typically appears during the first three years of life. The result of a neurological disorder that affects the functioning of the brain, autism impacts the normal development of the brain, leading to reduction in various degrees in the areas of social interaction and communication skills. Children and adults with autism typically have difficulties in verbal and non-verbal communication, social interactions, and leisure or play activities. The treatment has to be multifaceted including physiological, psychological and sociological integrated care in an environment radiating with kindness.

Today, a child who receives effective therapy and education has every hope of using his or her unique capacity to learn. Even some who are seriously mentally retarded can often acquire many self-help skills like cooking, dressing, doing the laundry and even handling money. For such children, greater independence and self-care may be primary training goals. Other youngsters may go on to learn basic academic skills like reading, writing and simple math. Many may reach high school and some may even earn college degrees. Like anyone else, their personal interests provide strong incentives to learn. How to give the incentive for such needs? There is a need of teaching with love.

Clearly, an important factor in developing a child's long-term potential for independence and success may require early intervention. The sooner a child begins to receive help, the more opportunities for learning are created. Furthermore, because a young child's brain is still forming, scientists believe that early intervention gives children a better chance of developing their full potential. Some institutions in India have facilities for the development of children as well as grown-ups.

Developmental approaches

Professionals have found that many children with autism learn best in an environment that builds on their skills and interests while accommodating their special needs. Programmes employing a developmental approach provide consistency and structure along with appropriate levels of stimulation. For example, predictable schedules of activities each day help children with autism adapt and organize their way of life. Using a certain area of the classroom for each activity helps students by making them familiar with what they are expected to do. For those with sensory problems, activities that sensitize or desensitize the child to certain kinds of stimulation may be especially helpful.

Management of autistic children

Once autism is diagnosed, it is essential that patients are given proper training to improve their behaviour and skills. There is need for creating institutions for training of teachers and parents. More often than not an autistic person requires personal care and personal training which demands that the patient-to-teacher ratio has to be low. Since most autistic children lose speech, well-equipped speech therapy centres are required to develop speech and communication skills. In spite of continuous training and care, autistic children cannot become totally independent. Hence there is need for having lifetime care centres with proper lodging and boarding facilities and homes. Initiatives are essential for creating training and lifetime care facilities. There is a need for separate schools in different parts of the country with well-trained teachers. At present such facilities are available only in large cities. Treatment has to be multifaceted including physiological, psychological and sociological integrated care.

Any disorder in human faculty such as autism increases dependence on others and reduces the self-esteem of the individual. Researchers must direct their efforts to bringing about a sense of equality amongst children affected by autism. Equality can be generated by prevention, early detection, appropriate training to acquire certain skills and engaging the minds of affected children in productive efforts to enable them to lead a normal life. This international conference is an important step towards finding a research-based solution for the causes, diagnostics and interventions required for the cure of autism.

Epilogue

COMMUNICATING SCIENCE

In nine chapters we have raced through various aspects of science and technology that will be of great importance to us in the twenty-first century, and have tried to understand, through technical knowhow as well as through social and economic linkages, how science can be used to make life easier and better. Some of you would have been familiar at least in part with what we have talked about, but may not have thought about these subjects in quite the same way; for some others it may all be new, and provide food for thought.

Writing about science is not easy. Precise explanations of scientific phenomena often require the support of complicated mathematical formulas or a long tabulation of researched facts. This may be boring or intimidating for people who are not well versed in the methods of science. On the other hand, if the information provided is simplified too much, those who have studied science and want to have more advanced knowledge about the newer developments might be disappointed. We have tried to strike a balance, providing as much information as possible without going into too many technicalities that a lay reader cannot relate to.

The other issue in science writing has to deal with accuracy of information. Nowadays it is possible to look up just about any scientific topic, from the H1N1 virus to the Chandrayaan mission, on the web. Unfortunately, a lot of what is available on the Net is not scientifically correct (though often it is full of scientific jargon!). In some scientific areas which are still emerging and not fully conclusive, some scientists propagate their own theories as the truth; this is a distortion of facts. But the bigger danger is in people sensationalizing scientific findings selectively and jumping to conclusions, without providing the basic facts or understanding the bigger picture. The media is particularly guilty of this practice.

Y.S. Rajan has addressed a number of these issues in his earlier writings on the challenges of science communication in the twenty-first century, an excerpt from which appears below. Dr Kalam too has addressed the issue of communicating science in his talks. Dr Kalam himself is a very good science communicator whose speeches are always alive with the possibilities of science and who is able to make people think about everyday matters in scientific terms through his simple scientific analogies.

Our endeavour in this book is to arouse the spirit of curiosity and scientific inquiry in every reader. When you put a lot of ice into your drink, even above the rim of the glass, why does the liquid not spill after the ice melts? Why does boiling water release so many bubbles? How does a big 20 litre mineral water jar sit inverted on the small vessel with the tap without overflowing? We would want you to look for scientific answers to all the interesting natural phenomena that takes place around you.

It has also become fashionable these days to question scientific achievements, or even the need for scientific exploration. Why must India waste so much money on the Chandrayaan mission when millions of Indians in rural areas are suffering? What good will going to the Moon do us? If you have a scientific bent of mind and a penchant for data, you will relish combating such anti-scientific and reactionary stances with the right statistics. How much is actually spent by the Government of India and the various state governments on rural development programmes each year?

How does this figure compare to what was spent on Chandrayaan? Is it the Chandrayaan project or the nuclear deal that prevents enough resources being available for rural development? It is important to ask the questions, even if you may not have all the answers.

This is how you can make science a part of your life, and enjoy the world that knowledge opens up to you, even if you are not a professionally trained scientist, technologist or medical doctor. There is a whole chain of science communicators across the globe; you can be one too, and link up to the world.

~

Here are some some extracts on science communication tasks for the twenty-first century from Y.S. Rajan's book *Empowering Indians with Economic, Business and Technology Strengths for the Twenty-first Century*.

Humanity is in a period of rapid change. Science and technology and several forms of social sciences and their applications have transformed human society to a state never before known in history. Probably such a statement would have sounded true if it were made 100 years ago as well! But in this period, a generation sees multiple changes and is impacted by various changes taking place at multiple locations in the world. These changes interact with each other, in turn stimulating newer changes. Lives of people are affected substantially by these changes—both beneficially and otherwise. On the one hand, the future of humanity looks bright, on the other very grim.

The problems facing humanity are not merely problems due to inequality, insecurity of employment, local environmental pollution or new forms of stress-based diseases. There are a number of basic ecological issues; if not addressed in time, these may threaten the Earth as a whole. There may be many catastrophic and irreversible changes.

Also tensions within societies (or nations) and between societies are erupting in newer forms. It will be difficult to deny that at least some of them are due to the irresponsibility or mischief of the media and/or geopolitics. Wounds in societies or the human psyche are opened (or reopened) citing some terrible injustices done many centuries ago. The information flow using modern technological gadgets spreads quickly. A lot of it can also be 'justified' under the pretext that history is written by the victorious. The economics of arms trade, narcotics trade, terrorist training and anti-terrorist training etc. have emerged as a significant part of the economies of many countries in addition to the usual military–industrial complexes and therefore linked up with profits, employment, political power, influence etc. On the other hand, advances in human knowledge about nature have progressed in many specialized fields. But along with tremendous progress there is also an emerging understanding about the limitations of super-specialized scientific pursuits and possible dangers arising out of such partitioned super-specializations. There is some search to understand the ancient knowledge systems, which were once ridiculed as superstitious. There are also eminent scientists who have come to a conclusion that mere dependence on 'science' alone cannot save the Earth in the future.

Thus we are at a crossroads. There is, therefore, a need to question the very basis of what 'science communication' is in this period of human history.

*

The methods of science are fairly well understood and imbibed in the system. Observation, data collection, analysis, hypothesis, tests of the possible results of the hypothesis by others, acceptance, modification or rejection of the hypothesis, replacement of old theories, new findings at a later period, and so on—it is a never-ending process of search for knowledge. It is not a single person who covers the whole chain. Several hundreds of well-qualified persons often work in very narrow areas in these chains. Very few have a total picture, even post facto. In addition, in the early part of the twentieth century, physics combined with mathematics has led to newer methods of science. These are thought experiments and mathematical equations. The solutions to the equations 'predict' the existence of a particle, or the way an electron 'moves'. Thus a conceptualization itself starts off as a scientific contribution and waits many years for a validation by actual experiment. During that period, it is still 'science' when the 'peer group' accepts it. Such a method has spread to other areas as well. Also in social sciences, say economics, there is no method of validating the way it would be done for physics or chemistry.

*

There are those in power (in politics, administration, military, justice or business) and those who influence decision-making (mediapersons, economists, opinion leaders in various fields etc.). Most of them are not well versed in any branch of science, nor do they keep up with the progress. This group of persons is crucial as their actions often determine the fates of millions of people and often the future of humanity or the world. They also have a genuine problem because one group of super-specialists pulls in one direction based on 'scientific' methods and another in another direction! What do science communicators do with these persons? It is not an easy question to answer. In reality most science communicators take a 'position' themselves amongst the myriad of 'opinions' and communicate them in a language with scientific terms. Very few will communicate different shades of 'opinions' looked at scientifically from different super-specialized subject areas or schools within the same subject area. It is also true that the decision-makers do not want to understand the complexity of the real situation and want a few 'definitive' options or even one conclusion. 'Can you tell me the conclusion—just one!' Otherwise, when the scientists explain the details 'on the one hand' and 'on the other hand', they look for a 'one-handed scientist'. In a period when scientific enterprise can lead to money and power, there are many willing 'one-handed scientists'! In turn what they say about various aspects of 'science' which are not necessarily in their narrow discipline area and also in areas where the interfaces of science is weak, they are taken by the 'public' and the 'powerful' as the final word. All of them believe that theirs is a 'scientific' conclusion.

There are other forms of science communication. There are science fictions and also popular writings on science. They serve their useful social purpose too, though they are not always 'scientifically' accurate. There are also writings about health hazards, which are often contradictory, though most of them quote scientific studies. For example, reports about smoking, the effects of tobacco, or alcohol or vitamins, would make one wonder what the truth is. Also take the arguments for or against dams or nuclear power. Many environmental issues are discussed as one-sided cases. Even issues like global warming have several schools.

*

These complexities and real life situations are pointed out because science communication cannot be viewed any more with a narrow perspective of science versus 'non-science', as is a tendency with some groups of communicators.

At this point, it will be useful to look at a quote from a commentary article by Sergei Kapitsa that appeared in *Current Science*:

> Without going into the subtle points of the philosophy of science, the distinction between knowledge and what one believes is sufficiently clear. A point one must bear in mind is that the message of the popularizer of science is in most cases taken on trust. The layman believes what he is told, as the proof is obtainable only through education. Thus the trust in the message of science demands great responsibility on the part of the messenger. On the other hand, the persuasive power of the media, especially of television, is remarkable, and the misuse of its potential is a matter of great ethical importance for society.

Another aspect of science communication is that it has to cater to the society and people, being a facilitator to help them lead a better life.

*

It may not always be advantageous to attack individual belief systems, unless there are socially dangerous. It is an irony of epistemology that the more we advance in science and empirical data, the more we know about the situation and at the same time there are more new unanswered questions. At any given point of time, a human being desires to be happy and safe and cannot wait indefinitely for answers to his or her questions. They form opinions and live with them. These opinions in general can be called a part of their value systems. The way the world is proceeding it is more important to develop value systems that would save the world and humanity rather than depend on the 'purity' of any human endeavour—science, religion, politics, culture etc. Therefore it appears that 'science communication' cannot stand alone. Also the connectivity due to advances in transport and communications are such that human thoughts and emotions are interconnected irretrievably and in an unprecedented manner. Therefore, the role of communicators in general, and that of science communicators as well, has to be transformed to face this new reality. We do not have answers as to what it should be. It will probably be an evolving one. It will be one that has to have a greater tolerance for various forms of human 'knowledge', however they are derived. It is not a question of abandoning scientific methods of exploring nature but of accepting that it is part of a complex web of human effort along with other forms of human effort. If not there is a real danger that science may be rejected by human societies, which will be a pity.

Dr Kalam himself symbolizes the Scientific Indian in the minds of many people. At the inauguration of the National Conference on Vision 2026—Challenges in Science Communication in New Delhi on 26 November 2006, he spoke about an Indian scientist who has spent much of his life in communicating science to people, especially children. The scientist is Prof. Yash Pal and the speech was delivered on the occasion of his eighty-first birthday.

Prof. Yash Pal and science

Prof. Yash Pal has made a substantial contribution to Indian science, science applications and science propagation. Whenever I see Prof. Yash Pal, I always see in front of me three events. The first one I remember is, when I was working with space scientists, periodically Prof. Yash Pal used to visit TERLS, and give beautiful suggestions to protect the delicate payloads from the shock generated by the rocket during take-off and the flight sequence. The suggestions were useful and I used to telephone to him how his suggestions totally worked during the integration of the sounding rocket payloads and flight. The second event took place in 1980, when I was busy with the SLV-3 launch at Sriharikota. Prof. Yash Pal was busy in setting up the Kytonn experiment, which is a tethered balloon for communication medium platforms. It had many technological innovations. This thought at that time was very new, today in many parts of the world it has become an operational system, particularly in the defence sector and hilly regions. The third event was, when Prof. Yash Pal saw my team working on multiple tasks and suggested that I must build a chicken-mesh antenna for the SITE experiment. This development should compete with two more engineering groups in the country. He gave stringent specifications and demanded that the antenna should be very cost-effective, and should be built and delivered within three months' time. It was done. This chicken-mesh antenna was intended to receive the educational programme broadcast through the communication satellite for remote villages in India.

When he was director of the Space Application Centre, and later as secretary general for UNISPACE and the chairman of UGC and in whatever task he undertook, his mission was to empower the children and the youth, particularly the rural village folk, with proper education and skills. NCERT has prepared the national curriculum framework under Prof. Yash Pal's leadership and modified the CBSE syllabus for promoting creative education at all levels through the application of the 'learning by doing' concept. He is the most sought-after person at the children's science congress, and the children seek answers from him in large numbers. He has a unique way of answering the questions of the children by constantly interacting with them and making them understand the answer through the discussion process itself. It is a beautiful scene to watch.

Eighty years, what does it mean? Indeed today, after completing eighty orbits around the Sun, Prof. Yash Pal is entering into the eighty-first orbit, and there are many more orbits to come. The eighty beautiful years with his cheerful family is indeed God's blessing and I wish him and his family all the best on this occasion.

Science communication: past, present and future

In the early days, due to the evolution of science itself in limited circles, science communication presented challenges with poor literacy and general knowledge levels of receptors and the absence of mediums of communication. Today, thanks to the efforts of visionaries like Prof. Yash Pal, I am seeing signs of science penetrating the socio-culturally diverse society of our country, touching every facet of day-to-day life. The scientists and science communicators have grown in number over the years. There have been initiatives from the government, NGOs and individuals in a broad spectrum of activities like popularizing science, training courses, lectures, fellowships and recognition of good works. Particularly, the programme titled *A Journey through the World of Science—Turning Point* conducted by Prof. Yash Pal and his team on the Doordarshan channel really kindled the imagination of the youth in the 1990s. Outreach has expanded substantially now through diverse media like print, audio-visual, folk, interactive and digital including CDs and Internet. I myself have addressed a few annual children science congresses, a highlight of the science communication calendar. The National Council of Museums, Kolkata is coordinating twenty-one science museums. Also there are five science cities in the country. Indian science communicators have used various modes of communication to reach out. The communication, information, digital and video technologies have expanded tremendously. TV and global communication provide opportunities in a way unprecedented to the people both literate and otherwise to learn the contemporary developments in science and technology and their applications.

The future challenges of science communication have several dimensions. The value of science has to be propagated to people at large and they should be made to realize the role played by science in their day-to-day life. Youngsters should be motivated to enquire into science. The innate fear that 'science is a difficult subject' should be removed from the minds of the children through easy-to-understand, interesting, creative presentations by the science communicators. Research, discoveries and development in one area of science that has to be communicated to other areas so that valuable products can be generated through convergence of technologies and a systematic science approach gets developed. We are already witnessing convergence of information, communication, bio-technology and nano sciences. A new science called Intelligent Bioscience is on the horizon which would lead to a disease-free, happy and more intelligent human habitat with longevity and high human capabilities. Convergence of bio–nano–info technologies can lead to the development of nano robots. Nano robots when they are injected into a patient, my expert friends say, will diagnose and deliver the treatment exclusively in the affected area and then get digested, as it is a DNA-based product. There are many more applications.

Motivating youngsters into science

In my many interactions with schoolchildren, parents, teachers and educationists, I have been told that our existing educational process tends to emphasize learning by memory rather than strengthening creativity. The essence of science and technology on the other hand is embedded in two of the most fundamental impulses: the desire to discover, and the desire to invent. It is vital that our education process nurtures and nourishes these two impulses.

It is not only lay persons who would learn from what science communicators have to say. Even scientists and technologists who necessarily have to be super-specialists to advance knowledge in their own particular areas have to learn about developments in other areas of science, and they can only do so through easily communicated science discussions. In addition, unlike in the past, the information explosion has led to a bombardment of easily accessible but often inauthentic scientific information. The scientific and academic community may have to create a respected cadre of persons who can be reliable science communicators and provide accurate information for scientific dissemination and further research.

Let us note what the Nobel Laureate Prof. Murray Gel Mann has to say about the emerging realities in his book *The Quark and the Jaguar: Adventures in the Simple and the Complex.*

Unfortunately, the information explosion is in great part a misinformation explosion. All of us are exposed to huge amounts of material, consisting of data, ideas, and conclusions—much of it wrong or misunderstood or just plain confused. There is a crying need for more intelligent commentary and review. We must attach a higher prestige to that very creative act, the writing of serious review articles and books that distinguish the reliable from the unreliable and systematize and encapsulate, in the form of reasonably successful theories and other schemata, what does seem reliable. If an academic publishes a novel research result at the frontier of knowledge in science or scholarship, he or she may reap a reward in the form of a professorship or a promotion, even if the result is later shown to be entirely wrong. However, clarifying the meaning of what has already been done (or picking out what is worth learning from what is not) is much less likely to advance an academic career. Humanity will be much better off when the reward structure is altered so that selection pressures on careers favour the sorting out of information as well as its acquisition . . . But how do we reconcile the critical examination of ideas, including the identification and labelling of error with tolerance—and even celebration and preservation—of cultural diversity? ... Yet the difficulty goes far deeper. Many of the local patterns of thought and behaviour are associated not only with harmful error and destructive particularism but specifically with harassment and persecution of those who espouse the universalizing scientific and secular culture, with its emphasis on rationality and the rights of the human individual. And yet it is within that very culture that one often finds people concerned, as a matter of principle, with the preservation of cultural diversity. Somehow the human race has to find ways to respect and make use of the great variety of cultural traditions and still resist the threats of disunity, oppression and obscurantism that some of those traditions present from time to time.

The future is full of challenges, or opportunities, whichever way you want to look at it. It is up to you to know more about the world around you, and to spread that knowledge to others, in your role as the Scientific Indian.